Elizabethan Humour

Elizabethan Humour

Edited by
CHRIS MEADS

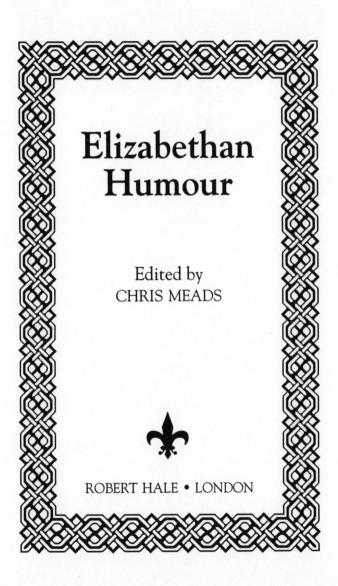

ROBERT HALE • LONDON

Preface and Selection © Chris Meads 1995
First published in Great Britain 1995

ISBN 0 7090 5665 6

Robert Hale Limited
Clerkenwell House
Clerkenwell Green
London EC1R 0HT

2 4 6 8 10 9 7 5 3 1

Printed in Great Britain by St Edmundsbury Press,
Bury St Edmunds, Suffolk.
Bound by Hunter & Foulis, Edinburgh

TO
The Perufer of this
Booke.

Who ere thou be, that comm'st to reade this Booke,
Come with a minde prepar'd to smile,
Or else be gone,
For here are none,
But toyes, loose houres to beguile.
And when th'art come, cast no disdainfull looke,
Nor looke of scorne upon our Lines:
For soone wee may,
Perchance repay
Such scorne into that face of thine.
But if thou canst sport at a harmlesse Jest;
If thou canst laugh (all frownes forgot),
If thou canst play,
With what we say,
And passe by that which likes thee not;
If no vaine haughty pride raigne in thy brest,
If thy cleane heart is purg'd from gall;
Then reade, tis free,
For such as thee,
To laugh, to sport, and play withall.

Preface

In 1603, the Venetian Ambassador in England reported to his masters that Queen Elizabeth, 'cannot attend to any discourse of Government and State, but delighteth to hear some of the 100 Merry Tales.' In what may have passed for her dotage, in what was in any case her last year of life, Elizabeth I took consolation in humorous tales from a book first compiled around the time her mother-to-be, Ann Boleyn, met her father Henry VIII. This same Elizabeth, was the queen who had often commanded private appearances by Richard Tarlton, the most famous stage comedian of his age, to raise her spirits, and this was the monarch who demonstrated her own caustic wit at Court.

The body of comic material presented here bounded by the term, 'Elizabethan', was a diverse, sometimes plagiarized, and oft reprinted canon. Take the compilation of Tarltons Jests, for example. Not published until 1611, twenty-two years after his death, these were jests and stories from the 1570s and 1580s which were still in print in 1628. The similar collection of The Jests of Scogin, the tales associated with Edward IV's jester were probably brought together almost a hundred years later in the 1560s and were still being published in the 1620s.

When the most coherent and best compiled collection of

7

'*Court, Camp, College, City and Country Jests*' came into being as A Banquet of Jests in 1630, it tacitly acknowledged its debt (by claiming its superiority!) to its rival publications from as early as Henry VII's time. *The book itself ran to six, ever larger, editions by the time of the Civil War.*

Although a more sophisticated and better produced book than most of its predecessors, it could not disguise its Elizabethan colours. It was an anonymous work, but claimed a connection with a king's jester, perhaps Archie Armstrong, thus placing the work in a long tradition from Scogin, through Will Summers, diverging to incorporate stage comedians such as Richard Tarlton, Will Kempe and Robert Armin, whose portrayal of the Fool in King Lear *may have contained a hint of Armstrong.*

Tarlton was the sort of stage clown so despised by Hamlet in his address to the players at Elsinore. As a member of the Queen's Players, his very appearance through the curtain rear-stage was sufficient to initiate titters in an audience – as one of the stories herein tells us. The comic actor, Robert Armin, affected a more scholarly approach to the craft of comedy, and he wrote a retrospective account of the exploits of various jesters and comic characters in A Nest of Ninnies *published in 1608. Less respectful of the emphasis scholastic was Scogin who marshalled all the wit at his command to proclaim that, 'a Master of Art is not worth a fart'.*

What follows is an edited selection of jokes, jests and amusing stories from the age of Shakespeare. Over the early modern period a good number of 'Jest Books' were printed – material collected under the name of the most famous comedians of the time, such as Richard Tarlton, or William Kempe, or simply anthologized collections of funny stories, jokes, and amusing dialogues between caricature characters. In addition there were opportunities to wax satirical in some of the 'docu-

mentary' or quasi-journalistic tracts which appeared as the sixteenth century progressed, examples of which have also been
included.

This is not a wholly representative selection in that the
many Latin and military jokes have been neglected, along with
many, many jests centring on fears of 'cuckoldry' and the
'cuckold's horns'. (Adultery does, however, remain well
represented as a theme!) There are many jests, the humour of
which must have lain in the telling, or wordplay obscured by
changes in pronunciation or association. All these have been
left to one side, as they tend to require more space for
explanation than the jest itself takes in the telling!

The spelling has been regularized and modernized for material which spans many years of change in the language itself.
This was the time when English itself was evolving with great
rapidity into a national tongue. The perennial wordplay perhaps reflects the fascination, excitement and desire to celebrate
the potential offered by this welter of newly coined words.

The stories themselves often defy modern punctuation,
syntactical, or grammatical convention; this reflects their no
doubt oral origins. They certainly give the lie to those who
seek to foist upon us the notion that English spelling, grammar
and punctuation were spontaneously and immaculately
conceived at some unspecified point in the past. In order to
aid the convention-blessed modern reader, speech punctuation
has been added, and full-stops, commas, exclamation and
question marks used in a more regular fashion than early
writers and printers. Thankfully, the punctuation, even when
inserted, does little to disguise the fluidity and fresh, anarchic
flexibility of the anecdotal style employed by the writers of
these jests and merry tales.

Humorous prose is an area of Elizabethan literature which
has remained unexplored, and largely unloved. It has been
perceived as something of an embarrassment, from the 'Golden

Age' of Shakespearian literature. Some of the anecdotes and jests which follow have not been reprinted for over 350 years, and others not seen the full light of day because of Victorian censorship applied to nineteenth-century antiquarian editions.

For all their reputed robustness there is, perhaps surprisingly, a good deal of euphemism employed by these raconteurs. Although more 'matter-of-fact' about all sorts of sexual and visceral matters, there is often less open bawdiness than is to be found in those more celebrated stage plays of Shakespeare and his contemporaries.

A few of the following extracts do bear traces of the future subtlety and irony for which the stereotypical 'British Sense of Humour' is internationally notorious. Some have pretensions to satire, but many are frankly puerile and demonstrate a juvenile fixation with bodily functions. They are often plainly bizarre, and some will seem outrageous to the sensibilities of the modern reader. Others, particularly some of the puns, are so lame they elicit the same, familiar groan they must always have done.

Yet many are the prototypes of our modern jokes, and they reveal recognizable anxieties and preoccupations in what was the early modern age. Tensions, particularly sexual tensions, abound, as do those arising from the growing disparities between the rural and the urban worlds.

Even the least amusing examples anthologized in the jest-books have a baffling charm and serve to remind us that what the nation finds hilarious has much to tell us about its culture, its fashions, its social preoccupations, and about the protean nature of what it takes to make us laugh.

An unequall Marriage

A young woman married to an old man, on the wedding-day was very sad and melancholy: which a neighbour of hers observing, spake merrily, and said, 'Be of good comfort neighbour, for an old horse will travel as long a journey, as a young one.'

'Ay,' saith she, fetching a great sigh, 'but not every day.'

A BANQUET OF JESTS

A Knavish answere of an unhappy country wench to a foolish yong fellow

A certain idle-headed young man, that loved to hear himself speak, though it were of matter to little purpose, riding upon a fair day to a market town, overtook by chance, among other creatures of her kind, an indifferent well-favoured and well-grown country wench, whom singling by herself as much as she could, he fell to commune with, in an odd manner of love-making when, beginning very low, marking her new shod feet, hanging over her dossers [horse panniers], began with this commendation:

'Truly, sister, you have a very fine foot there.'

'Yea, sir,' (quoth the wench), 'that I have; a couple.'

The young man thinking to show some little wit, in a scoff replied with this speech: 'But are they twins, sister? Were they both born at one time?'

'No, indeed, sir,' (quoth the wench), 'there hath been a man borne betwixt them!'

Wherewith her neighbours that rode by her, falling into a laughing, made him find that she was a married wife: which being contrary to his expectation, being much troubled with her answer, with lack of wit to reply, galloped away with a flea in his ear.

PASQUILS JESTS

11

Of the gentle-woman that said to a gentleman: you have a beard above and none beneath.

A young gentleman of the age of twenty year, somewhat disposed to mirth and gay, on a time talked with a gentle-woman which was right wise and also merry.

This gentlewoman, as she talked with him, happened to look upon his beard which was but young and some-what grown upon the overlip, and but little grown beneath as all other young mens' beards commonly used to grow, and said to him thus: 'Sir ye have a beard above and none beneath.'

And he, hearing her say so, said in sport: 'Mistress, ye have a beard beneath and none above.'

'Marry,' quoth she, 'then set the one against tother!'

Which answer made the gentleman so abashed, that he had not one word to answer.

AN HUNDRED MERRY TALES

An English man, and a French man courting a Lady

An English man, and a French man going to visit a handsome Lady: the French man much taken with her features at first sight, stepped forward before the other and kiss'd her.

At which, the English Gentleman greatly incensed, as being of his acquaintance told him such manners favoured of the French impudence, and misbecame him here.

But he thinking to excuse himself, and not well acquainted with our English phrase, repli'd, 'No harm done, good Monsieur; for now I have kissed her before, you have good leave to kiss her behind.' Meaning after.

A BANQUET OF JESTS

Of a yong Gentleman that would have kissed a mayd with a long nose

A young Gentleman, none of the wisest, would have kissed a fair maid that had something of a long nose, and said: 'How should I kiss you? Your nose is so long that our lips cannot meet.'

The Maid waxing angry in mind said: 'If you cannot kiss my mouth, sir, for my nose, you may kiss me there whereas I have never a nose!'

PASQUILS JESTS

Two old widows sitting over a cup of ale in a Winter's night, entered into a discussion of their dead husbands, and after the ripping up of their good and bad qualities, saith one of them to her maid, 'I prethee wench, reach us another light, for my husband (God rest his soul) above all things loved to see good lights about the house. God grant him light everlasting.'

'And I pray you neighbour,' (saith the other), 'let the

13

maid lay on some more coals, or stir up the fire, for my husband in his lifetime ever loved to see a good fire. God grant him fire everlasting.'

A BANQUET OF JESTS

A woman had a husband that used to come home often disguised [drunk] and sometimes to lie along the floor; and still when she offered to raise him from the ground he would not be removed but answered, 'The tenement is mine own; I pay rent for it, and I may lie where I list.'

Some few nights after, coming home in the like taking he sat down in a chair before the fire and fell sleep. The woman would have waked him but could not, and therefore went up to bed, in which she was scarcely warm, but the Maid cried out aloud, 'Mistress, Mistress! My master is fallen out of the chair, and lies in the midst of the fire!'

Which she hearing, lay still and answered, 'Let him alone. For as long as he pays rent for the house – he may lie where he will . . . .'

A BANQUET OF JESTS

One asked why men and their wives did not agree better nowadays. It was answered, men were now more learned, and did know that it was false concord that the masculine and feminine gender should agree at all.

CONCEITS, CLINCHES, FLASHES AND WHIMZIES

A man being upon the sea in a great tempest, and danger of shipwreck, was commanded to cast something forth that might best be spared, to lighten the burden of the ship; who answered, he would cast out his wife.

CERTAYNE CONCEYTS AND JEASTS

On a Court Lady
A Court lady at dinner amongst divers gallants, speaking of her age, said she was but forty years old.

When, presently one of them rounded his next neighbour in the ear: 'It would require,' (saith he), 'a stronger faith than I have in me to believe this.'

But he made answer, 'I must needs believe her, for I have heard her say so, any time these ten years.'

A BANQUET OF JESTS

A Lady that was painted [heavily made-up] told a Gentleman she desired much to have her picture done to the life; to which he answered: 'You need not that, Madam, for you are a picture to the life already.'

CONCEITS, CLINCHES, FLASHES AND WHIMZIES

Of a Barber new married
A spruce barber having married a young smug lass, and presuming on his wit (the same that he was used to vent upon his customers, when they were trimming) on the wedding night, they were no sooner laid in bed and the company gone, but he thinking to put a trick upon her

15

because he thought her somewhat simple, made proffer to rise from her.

She asked him his reason. He made answer, because he took her to be a virgin and was loth to put her to too much pains, he had an instrument in his case which he would instantly fetch, to prevent all such inconveniences.

She, when she heard this, clasped him close in her arms, and said, 'Sweet husband lie down again, there is no such need. My father's journey-man hath taken such order with me many months ago, that you may very well spare that labour.'

A BANQUET OF JESTS

Of a married man who had but one eye
A man with one eye, thinking he had married a virgin, and finding that she had before been visited, grew into very bitter language, upbraiding her of inchastity, saying, she came not unto him (as he expected), sound and perfect.

The woman made answer, 'Why shouldst thou look, that I should come so unto thee, that art thyself neither sound nor perfect, being half blind, as wanting one of thine eyes.

'Ay, but woman,' (saith he), 'this hurt which I have, I received from mine enemy.'

She answered him again; 'Why, and know thou man, that this flaw which I have got, I received from my friend!'

A BANQUET OF JESTS

Of a Locksmith and his wife

A locksmith, jealous of his wife (and that not without cause), had often read her lectures, telling her how precious a woman's chastity was, and how honourable the state of matrimony. And, being best acquainted with his own trade, he would draw his comparisons from that when thinking to hit the nail on the head.

He proceeded to hammer out his mind, as followeth: 'Women ought to keep a latch upon the door, their breasts bolted, their hearts locked, and double-locked, their bodies neither to be wrested by force, nor opened by picklocks . . . .' and the like.

She, being vexed with the tediousness of his talk, broke out into passion and said, 'Here is a coil indeed with your bars, your bolts, and your locks, when there is not a tapster nor an ostler that I know but hath as good a key as the best smith of you all, to open.'

A BANQUET OF JESTS

One asked a painter why, seeing that he could draw such excellent proportions, he begot such deformed children. He answered: 'I draw at the one in the day, but I work at the other in the night.'

CERTAYNE CONCEYTS AND JEASTS

One asked what the reason was that few women lov'd to eat eggs. It was answered, because they cannot endure to bear the yoke.

CONCEITS, CLINCHES, FLASHES AND WHIMZIES

How to make an Egge flye about, a merry conclusion
To do this, take a goose egg, and after opening and cleansing of it, take a bat that flyeth in the evening, which put into the shell, then glue it fast about on the top, and the bat will so fly away with it, which perhaps will be thought of some to fly about in the air of itself.

A BRIEFE TREATISE OF NATURALL & ARTIFICIALL CONCLUSIONS

How to make a loafe of bread newe set upon the Table to leape of
To do this, take a quill filling the same with quicksilver, and stopping it close, thrust the same after into a hot loaf new drawn out of the oven, and the loaf will by and by dance on the table.

A BRIEFE TREATISE OF NATURALL & ARTIFICIALL CONCLUSIONS

How Scogin sold powder to kill fleas

Scogin diverse times did lack money, and could not tell what shift to make. At last, he thought to play the physician, and did fill a box full of the powder of a rotten post; and on a Sunday he went to a Parish Church, and told the wives that he had a powder to kill up all the fleas in the country, and every wife bought a pennyworth; and Scogin went his way, ere Mass was done. The wives went home, and cast the powder into their beds and in their chambers, and the fleas continued still.

On a time, Scogin came to the same Church on a Sunday, and when the wives had espied him, the one said to the other: 'This is he that deceived us with the powder to kill fleas.'

'See,' said the one to the other, 'this is the selfsame person.'

When Mass was done, the wives gathered about Scogin and said, 'You be an honest man to deceive us with the powder to kill fleas.'

'Why,' said Scogin, 'are not your fleas all dead?'

'We have more now,' (said they), 'than ever we had.'

'I marvel of that,' said Scogin, 'I am sure you did not use the medicine as you should have done.'

They said, 'We did cast it in our beds and in our chambers.'

'Aye,' said he, 'there be a sort of fools that will buy a thing, and will not ask what they should do with it. I tell you all, that you should have taken every flea by the neck, and then they would gape; and then you should have cast a little of the powder into every flea's mouth, and so you should have killed them all!'

Then said the wives; we have not only lost our money, but we are mocked for our labour.

THE JESTS OF SCOGIN

A joiner on a time took a pill, and it so wrought with him, that he had forty stools in a minute of an hour.
CONCEITS, CLINCHES, FLASHES AND WHIMZIES

One met his friend in the street, and told him he was sorry to see him look so ill, asking what he ailed.

He replied that he was now well amended, but he had been lately sick of the Pox.

'What pox? The small pox?' said his friend.

'Nay,' quoth the other, 'my mind was not so base, for I had the biggest pox that I could get for my money.'
TAYLORS WIT AND MIRTH

How Scogin gave one a medecine to make him go to it
On a time, there did a young man come to Scogin to have a medicine, saying, 'Sir, I would have a medicine to make me go to it lustily.'

He meant Venus' acts; Scogin did give him an extreme purgation.

The young man went to bed with his lemman [lover]. Within a while, his belly began to rumble, and there was no remedy, but he must needs go to it so long, that he did defile both the chamber and the bed, so that he and his lemman bathed themselves that night in dirt.

Wherefore it is good for all men, when they ask counsel of any man, to be plain in his words, and not to speak in parables.
THE JESTS OF SCOGIN

A barber coming finical about a gentleman, was (as most of them are) terrible full of talk. At length he found the leisure to ask him how he would be trimmed.

'Marry, my friend,' replied the gentleman, 'if thou canst possibly – do it in silence.'

A BANQUET OF JESTS

Of a Barbar

A fellow that was trimming [being trimmed], seeing the barber (who it seems had got a cup too much) turn aside and piss in the chimney, asked him what reason he had to offend his shop so, and annoy it with the smell.

'O, no matter,' replied the barber, 'for I mean to leave it next quarter.'

Upon these words, the fellow presently finds fault with some linen that was about him, and whilst the barber steps up the stairs for cleaner, he untrusseth in the chimney.

Which the barber at his return perceiving: 'Now fie for shame friend,' saith he, 'why have you thus play'd the sloven in my shop?'

'Marry,' answered the fellow, 'you pissed in it, because you meant to leave it next quarter, and I have done as you see, because I purpose to leave it straightway!'

A BANQUET OF JESTS

One said that some tailors were like woodcocks, because they lived by their long bills.

CONCEITS, CLINCHES, FLASHES AND WHIMZIES

One commending a tailor for his dexterity in his profession, another standing by ratified his opinion, saying tailors had their business at their fingers ends.

CONCEITS, CLINCHES, FLASHES AND WHIMZIES

21

A Smith, said one, is the most pragmatical fellow under the sun, for he hath always many irons in the fire.

CONCEITS, CLINCHES, FLASHES AND WHIMZIES

A Chandler's shop was one night broke open and robbed. In the morning he sat, melancholy. One of his next neighbours, seeing him so sad, demanded of him the cause, to whom (fetching a great sigh), 'Ah Gossip,' (saith he), 'this night my shop hath been rifled and I find missing a whole gross of candles.'

'Marry, a great loss indeed, neighbour. What! a whole gross of candles? But take it not to heart, for there is no doubt but that in good time they will be brought to light.'

A BANQUET OF JESTS

The Good advice of an Host

A company of my acquaintance, coming to an Inn in Cambridge (and having stayed somewhat long), some of them desired the rest of their company to make haste, for they must be gone.

'Why,' saith the Host, 'the best way to be *gone* is to drink hard!'

A BANQUET OF JESTS

A Drunkard and a Signe-post

Two country men keeping company till night, one of their heels were lighter than his head, and going under a sign-post, he lifted his leg very high. The other asked why he did so. He told him, it was to go over the stile, and pointed to the sign.

'Thou fool,' replied his friend, 'it is a sign.'

'A sign!' quoth hee, 'What sign?'

'Marry,' answered he again, 'a sign thou art terribly drunk!'

A BANQUET OF JESTS

Certain Gallants being at a tavern, where they spar'd no liquor, insomuch that all were well entered; but one whose head was somewhat weaker, and therefore lighter, did nothing but spew, and calling for a reckoning, 'Why,' says one of his friends, 'cannot you tell, that have so often cast up what you have drunk?'

CONCEITS, CLINCHES, FLASHES AND WHIMZIES

One said it was no great matter what a drunkard said in his drink, for he seldom spake anything that he could stand to.

CONCEITS, CLINCHES, FLASHES AND WHIMZIES

One meeting a drunkard reeling in the street, bade him stand up like a man, who answered him that for his own part *he* could stand well enough, but he could not make his shoes stand . . . .

A BANQUET OF JESTS

Tapsters, said one, should be men of great esteem, because they are men not only of a high calling, but also of great reckoning.

CONCEITS, CLINCHES, FLASHES AND WHIMZIES

The Eight Kinds of Drunkenness

Nor have we one or two kinds of drunkards only, but eight kinds.

The first is ape drunk, and he leaps, and sings, and haloos, and danceth for the heavens.

The second is lion drunk, and he flings the pots about the house, calls his hostess whore, breaks the glass windows with his dagger, and is apt to quarrel with any man that speaks to him.

The third is swine drunk, heavy, lumpish, and sleepy, and cries for a little more drink and a few more clothes.

The fourth is sheep drunk, wise in his own conceit when he cannot bring forth a right word.

The fifth is maudlin drunk when a fellow will weep for kindness in the midst of his ale, and kiss you saying, 'By God, captain, I love thee: go thy ways, thou dost not think so often of me as I do of thee: I would (if it pleased God) I could not love thee so well as I do.' And then he puts his finger in his eye and cries.

The sixth is martin [monkey] drunk, when a man is drunk and drinks himself sober ere he stir.

The seventh is goat drunk, when in his drunkenness, he hath no mind but on lechery.

The eighth is fox drunk, when he is crafty drunk as many of the Dutchmen be, that will never bargain but when they are drunk.

All these species and more I have seen practised in one company at one sitting, when I have been permitted to remain sober amongst them, only to note their several humours. He that plies any one of them hard it will make him to write admirable verses, and to have a deep casting head though he were never so very a dunce before.

PIERCE PENNILESSE HIS SUPPLICATION TO THE DEVIL

Then came a drunken Dutch man
And he would have a touch man,
But he soon took too much, man
Which made them after rue:
He drank so long as I suppose,
Till great drops fell from his nose,
And like a beast befouled his hose.

JOAN'S ALE IS NEW

An jest made by Will Sommers
'Tell me,' says Will, 'if you can: what is it that being born without life, head, lip or eye, yet doth run roaring through the world till it die?'

'This is a wonder,' quoth the King, 'and no question. I know it not.'

'Why,' quoth Will, 'it is a fart!'

At this the King laughed heartily, and was exceeding merry.

A NEST OF NINNIES

How Scogin let a fart, and said it was worth forty pounds
The time that Scogin was conversant both in the King's chamber and in the Queen's, Scogin would peek here and there about in the Queen's chamber or lodging.

The Queen by custom (as most commonly all great women and ladies and gentlewomen do) she let a fart, saying: 'The same is worth to me twenty pounds.'

Scogin, hearing this, girt out a fart like a horse or mare, saying : 'If that fart be so dear of twenty pound, my fart is worth forty pounds!'

Here a man may see that a knave may do that which an honest man may not speak.

THE JESTS OF SCOGIN

This Earl of Oxford, making of his low obeisance to
Queen Elizabeth, happened to let a fart, at which he was
so abashed and ashamed that he went to travel, seven
years.

On his return the Queen welcomed him home, and
said, 'My Lord, I had forgot the fart.'

BRIEF LIVES

One passing through Cheapside, a poor woman desired
his charity; he disregarding the woman, kept on walking,
and by and by let a fart. The woman, hearing it, said,
much good may it do your worship; he, hearing her say
so, turns back and gives her a tester [a sixpence]. She
thanked him, and told his worship it was a bad wind, that
did blow nobody good.

CONCEITS, CLINCHES, FLASHES AND WHIMZIES

Of a Dwarfe
A dwarf was observed all the Summer long, never to walk
abroad without a nosegay in his hand, nor in the Winter,
but with a pair of perfum'd gloves.

One that had long noted it, demanded of a Gentleman
a friend of his, what he thought the reason thereof might
be. To whom he answered that, in his opinion, he did it
not without great advisement and consideration.

'For,' saith he, 'most necessary it is that he should
carry still some sweet thing in his hand to smell unto,
whose nose is level with every man's tail whom he followeth.'

A BANQUET OF JESTS

A certain boisterous rustic, yet prompt and conceyted, travelling on the way with a long pike-staff on his neck, was suddenly and furiously assaulted by a great mastiff-dog, which came upon him with open mouth and violence, as if he would at once devour him.

Who presently, to withstand the danger by rescue of himself, runs the pike and sharp end of his staff into his throat, whereupon he presently died.

Which the owner thereof seeing, comes eagerly unto him, and between threatening and chiding asked him, why he struck him not rather with the blunt end of his staff.

'Why, Sir,' (quoth he), 'because your dog ran not at me with his tail.'

CERTAYNE CONCEYTS AND JEASTS

A country fellow asking which way he might go to Bedlam, a citizen told him the nearest way was to be mad.

CONCEITS, CLINCHES, FLASHES AND WHIMZIES

Of seeing the Winde
Two country fellows meeting, one asked the other, 'What news?'

He answered, he knew no other news, but that he saw a great wind last Friday.

'See a wind?' quoth the other, 'I prethee what was it like?'

'Marry,' (saith he), 'it was like to have blown down my house!'

A BANQUET OF JESTS

One being asked what countryman he was, he answered, a Middlesex man. The other told him being he was neither of the male sex nor of the female sex, but of a middlesex, he must then be a Hermaphrodite.

CONCEITS, CLINCHES, FLASHES AND WHIMZIES.

An ignorant mistake
A country fellow being call'd as witness about a piece of land in controversy: saith the Judge to him, friend, how do you call the water that runs on the South side of such a close?

'My Lord,' (quoth the fellow), 'our water comes without calling.'

A BANQUET OF JESTS

Two Plasterers being at work for me at my house in Southwark, did many times patch and daub out part of their day's labour with prating; which I, being digging in my garden, did overhear that their chat was of their wives, and how that, 'If I were able,' (quoth one), 'my wife should ride in pomp through London as I saw a Countess ride yesterday.'

'Why,' quoth the other, 'how did she ride, I pray?'

'Marry,' said he, 'in State; in her Horse-litter.'

'O base!' quoth the other, 'Horselitter? I protest, as poor a man as I am, I would have allowed my wife a three-penny truss of clean straw.'

TAYLORS WIT AND MIRTH

Of the blynde man and his boye

A certain poor blind man in the country was led by a curst boy to an house where a wedding was: so the honest folks gave him meat, and at last one gave him a leg of a good fat goose; which the boy receiving kept aside and did eat it up himself.

Anon the blind man said: 'Jack, where is the leg of the goose?'

'What goose?' (quoth the boy), 'I have none.'

'Thou liest,' (quoth the blind man), 'I did smell it.'

And so they went forth chiding together, till the shrewd boy led the poor man against a post, where hitting his brow a great blow, he cried out: 'A whoreson boy, what hast thou done?'

'Why,' (quoth the boy), 'could you not smell the post that was so near, as well as the goose that was so far from your nose?'

MERY TALES, WITTIE QUESTIONS, AND QUICKE ANSWERES

A serving man, bringing a brace of greyhounds from his master to a knight, a friend of his and a near-neighbour: the knight asked him whether they were good dogs or no.

'Good dogs?' (saith the fellow), 'I will assure you, for this,' (pointing to the one of them), 'he is the best dog that ever ran with four legs upon the earth. And see you this other? He is three times better than he.'
A BANQUET OF JESTS

The Second Tale of the Mad Men of Gottam
There was a man of Gottam did ride to the market with two bushels of wheat, and because his horse should not bear heavy, he carried his corn upon his own neck, and did ride upon his horse, because his horse should not carry too heavy a burden. Judge you which the wisest, his horse or himself.

The Third Tale of the Mad Men of Gottam
On a time, the men of Gottam would have penned in the cuckoo, whereby she should sing all the year, and in the midst of the town they made a hedge round in compass, and they had got a cuckoo, and had put her into it, and said: 'Sing here all the year, and thou shalt lack neither meat nor drink.'

The cuckoo, as soon as she perceived her self encompassed within the hedge, flew away.

'A vengeance on her,' said they: 'We made not our hedge high enough.'

The Fourth Tale of the Mad Men of Gottam
There was a man of Gottam, the which went to the market to Nottingham, to sell cheese, and as he was going down the hill to Nottingham-bridge, one of his cheeses did fall out of his wallet, and ran down the hill.

'A whorsons,' said the fellow: 'Can you run to the market alone? I will send the one after the other of you.'

Then he lay down his wallet, and took the cheeses, and did tumble them down the hill one after another, and some ran into one bush, and some into another; and at last he said, 'I charge you all meet me in the market-place.'

And when the fellow came to the market-place to meet his cheeses, he stayed there, till the market was almost done. Then he went about and did enquire of his neighbours and other men, if they did see his cheeses come to the market.

'Who should bring them?' said one of the market-men.

'Marry, themselves,' said the fellow, 'they knew the way well enough.' He said: 'A vengeance on them all. I did fear to see my cheeses run so fast, that they would run beyond the market; I am now fully persuaded, that they be almost at York.'

Whereupon he forthwith hired a horse to ride after to York to seek his cheeses, where they were not. But to this day no man could tell him of his cheeses.

MERY TALES OF THE MAD MEN OF GOTTAM

Horse keepers and ostlers – let the world go which way it will, though there be never so much alteration in times and persons – are still stable men.

CONCEITS, CLINCHES, FLASHES AND WHIMZIES

One coming into Smithfield on a Friday Market called to a horse-courser aloud, and said, 'I prethee, my friend. How go horses today?'

To whom he answered, 'Marry, as you see – some amble, some trot and some gallop!'

A BANQUET OF JESTS

He that buys a horse in Smithfield, and does not look upon him before he buy him, with a pair of spectacles, makes his horse and himself a pair of sorrowful spectacles, for others to look on.

CONCEITS, CLINCHES, FLASHES AND WHIMZIES

How to make that a horse maie not goe through a streate
Take the guts of a wolf, and lay them o'erthwart the street, and cover them with earth or sand, and he will not go that way, as long as the guts do lie there. *Probatum est.*

A BRIEFE TREATISE OF NATURALL & ARTIFICIALL CONCLUSIONS

A Horse stealer
A fellow for stealing of a horse, was apprehended, arraigned, convicted, and executed: the question being made, why this man was hanged. It was answered, 'For stealing a horse.'

'Nay,' saith the other, 'I will assure you, no such matter. He was hanged for being taken; for had he stolen an hundred and never been taken, he might have been alive at this day.'

A BANQUET OF JESTS

One passing by and seeing a poor fellow in a very cold morning upon the gallows in his shirt and, after a short confession, ready to be turned off the ladder: 'Alas, poor man,' (saith hee), 'I much pity him. He will stand so long yonder in the cold, that I am afraid he will go near to catch his death.'

A BANQUET OF JESTS

Of Rape Seed

A handsome young fellow having seen a play at The Curtain, comes to William Rowley after the play was done, and entreated him if his leisure served, that he might give him a pottle of wine, to be better acquainted with him. He thanked him, and told him, if he pleased to go as far as The Kings Head at the Spittle-gate, he would, as soon as he had made himself ready, follow him and accept of his kindness.

He did so, but the wine seeming tedious betwixt two, and the rather because the young fellow could entertain no discourse, Rowley beckoned to an honest fellow over the way to come and keep them company, who promised to be with them instantly, but not coming at the second or third calling. At last he appears in the room, where William Rowley begins to chide him because be stayed so long. He presently craved pardon and begins to excuse himself, that he had been abroad to buy rape-seed, and that he stayed to feed his birds.

At the very word of 'rape-seed', the man rose from the table with a changed countenance, being very much discontented, and said, 'Master Rowley, I came in courtesy

33

to desire your acquaintance, and to bestow the wine upon you, not thinking you would have called this fellow up to taunt me so bitterly.'

They wondering what he meant, he proceeded. 'Tis true indeed; the last Sessions I was arraigned at Newgate for a rape, but I thank God I came off like an honest man, little thinking to be twitted of it here.'

Both began to excuse themselves, as not knowing any such thing, as well as they might, but he that gave the offence, thinking the better to express his innocence: 'Young Gentleman,' saith hee, 'to express how far I was from wronging you, look you here. As I have rape-seed in one pocket for one bird, so here is hemp-seed on this side for another.'

At which word, hemp-seed, saith the young man, 'Why villain, doest thou think I have deserved hanging?' And took up the pot to fling at his head, but his hand was stayed and as error and mistake began the quarrel, so wine ended it!

A BANQUET OF JESTS

A Merry Jest how Ned Browne's Wife was Crossbitten in her own art

I remember once that I, supposing to crossbite a gentleman who had some ten pound in his sleeve, left my wife to perform the accident, who in the end was crossbitten herself. And thus it fell out. She compacted with a hooker, and having before bargained with the gentleman to tell her tales in her ear all night, he came according to promise, who, having supped and going to bed, was advised by my wife to lay his clothes in the window, where the hooker's crome [grappling hook] might crossbite them from him, yet secretly intending before in the night time to steal his money forth of his sleeve.

They, being in bed together, slept soundly: yet such was his chance, that he suddenly wakened long before her, and being sore troubled with a lask [diarrhoea], rose up and made a double use of his chamber pot. That done, he intended to throw it forth at the window, which the better to perform, he first removed his clothes from thence; at which instant the spring of the window rose up of the own accord.

This suddenly amazed him so, that he leapt back, leaving the chamber pot still standing in the window, fearing that the Devil had been at hand. By and by he espied a fair iron crome come marching in at the window, which instead of the doublet and hose he sought for suddenly took hold of that homely service in the member vessel, and so plucked goodman jordan with all its contents down pat on the curber's pate.

Never was gentle angler so dressed, for his face, his head, and his neck were all besmeared with the soft Sir Reverence, so as he stunk worse than a jakes-farmer. The gentleman, hearing one cry out, and seeing his mess of altogether so strangely taken away, began to take heart to him, and looking out perceived the curber lie almost brained, almost drowned, and well near poisoned therewith; whereat, laughing heartily to himself, he put on his own clothes, and got him secretly away, laying my wife's clothing in the same place, which the gentle angler soon after took. But never could she get them again till this day.

THE BLACK BOOK'S MESSENGER

An answer from a Jaques Farmer

Divers Gentlemen walking the streets somewhat late, where the 'Gold-finders' were at work.

'Fie fellows,' say they, 'what a beastly stink do you make?'

To whom one of the most ancient amongst them replied: 'If Gentlemen, you, or such as you, keep your tails stopped, you should not now need for to stop your noses!'

A BANQUET OF JESTS

Of him that dreamed he fonde golde

There was a man that said in company upon a time, how he dreamed on a night, that the devil led him in to a field to dig for gold.

When he had found the gold, the devil said, 'Thou canst not carry it away now, but mark the place, that thou mayst fetch it another time.'

'What mark shall I make?' quoth the man.

'Shyte over it,' quoth the devil, 'for that shall cause every man to shun the place, and so it shall be a special knowledge.'

The man was content and did so but when he awaked out of his sleep, he perceived that he had foul defiled his bed. Thus between stink and dirt up he rose, and made him ready to go forth: and last of all he put on his bonnet, wherein also the same night the cat had shit.

Thus his golden dream turned all to dirt.

MERY TALES, WITTIE QUESTIONS, AND QUICKE
ANSWERES

A man walking the street let a great fart, upon which he jestingly said: 'Crack me that nut!'

It being heard of a waggish wench that was in a chamber over his head, who being well provided at that time with a 'perfum'd' chamber pot, throws it out of the window upon his head saying, 'There's the kernel of your nut, sir!'

CONCEITS, CLINCHES, FLASHES AND WHIMZIES

How merry Andrew served another that would have put him down in his merry sayings

Andrew once was at supper with his friends, and among the company there was one that spited at his jests and merry conceits. After supper they fell to reasoning among themselves which was the most reverent part of a man's body. One said the eye; another, the nose; a third said, the leg: but Andrew, knowing that he that spited him would name the contrary, said, the mouth was the most reverent of all.

'Nay,' (quoth the other), 'the part we sit on is the most reverent.'

And because they all marvelled why he should say so, he made this reason: that he was most honourable that was the first set, and the part that he named was, first set. Which saying contented them all, and grieved Andrew.

The next day they all met again, and Andrew, coming last, found them all sitting together; and when he had saluted them all but his enemy, he turned his backside to him, and let a great fart in his face.

At which the fellow being mightily angry, said: 'Walk, knave, with a mischief! Where has thou been brought up?'

'Why disdainest thou?' quoth Andrew. 'If I had saluted thee with my mouth, thou wouldst have saluted me again, and now, when I salute thee with that part that by thy own saying is most honourable, thou callest me knave.'

Then the company fell a-laughing at this jest heartily.

PASQUILS JESTS

An Epitaph

One Master Dumbelow died of the wind colic upon whom one writ the Epitaph:

> Dead is Master Dumbelow
> Will you the reason know?
> Could his tail have but spoken,
> His heart had not broken.

A BANQUET OF JESTS

Tarlton's Jest of a pippin

At the Bull in Bishop-gate-street, where the Queen's Players oftentimes played, Tarlton coming on the stage, one from the gallery threw a pippin at him.

Tarlton took up the pip, and looking on it, made this suddden jest :

> Pip in, or nose in, choose you whether,
> Put yours in, ere I put in the other.
> Pippin you have put in: then, for my grace,
> Would I might put your nose in another place.

TARLTONS JESTS

A Tale of Wise Justice

Amongst other choleric wise justices, he was one, that having a play presented before him and his township by Tarlton and the rest of his fellows, Her Majesty's Servants, and they were now entering into their first merriment, as they call it, the people began exceedingly to laugh when Tarlton first peeped out his head. Whereat the Justice, not a little moved, and seeing with his becks and nods he could not make them cease, he went with his staff and beat them round about unmercifully on the bare pates, in that they, being but farmers and poor country hinds would presume to laugh at the Queen's Men, and make no more account of her cloth in his presence.

PIERCE PENNILESSE HIS SUPPLICATION TO THE DEVIL

Richard Burbidge and William Shakespeare

Upon a time when Burbidge played Richard III there was a citizen grew so far in liking with him that before she went from the play she appointed him to come that night unto her, by the name of 'Richard the Third'.

Shakespeare overhearing their conclusion went before, was entertained, and at his game ere Burbidge came. Then message being brought that 'Richard the Third' at the door, Shakespeare caused return to be made that William the Conqueror was before Richard III. (Shakespeare's name was William).

MANNINGHAM'S DIARY

A certain Player being sick, and lying upon his death-bed, the Priest came unto him, and exhorted him to make his will, which he said he would most willingly and quickly do: 'For,' (quoth he), 'I have nothing but two geldings to dispose, and I bequeath and give them to the Knights and Barons of the Land.'

And when the Priest asked him, why he gave them not rather to the poor, he answered: 'I do as you teach us, to be imitators of God; and he hath given all to the rich, and nothing to the poor, and therefore I will follow him, in doing the like.'

CERTAYNE CONCEYTS AND JEASTS

Of a Young Nip that Cunningly Beguiled an Ancient
Professor of that Trade, and his Quean with him, at a Play
A good fellow that was newly entered into the nipping
craft [cutting purses], and not as yet attained to any
acquaintance with the chief and cunning masters of that
trade, in the Christmas holidays last came to see a play at
the Bull within Bishopgate, there to take his benefit as
time and place would permit him.

Not long had he stayed in the press but he had gotten
a young man's purse out of his pocket which, when he
had, he stepped into the stable to take out the money,
and to convey away the purse. But looking on his com-
modity he found nothing therein but white counters, a
thimble and a broken threepence, which belike the
fellow that owned it had done of purpose to deceive the
cutpurse withal, or else had played at the cards for counters and so carried his winnings about him till his next
sitting to play.

Somewhat displeased to be so overtaken he looked
aside, and spied a lusty youth entering at the door, and
his drab ['quean', 'trug', his female companion] with him.
This fellow he had heard to be one of the finest nippers
about the town, and ever carried his quean with him, for
conveyance when the stratagem was performed. He puts
up the counters into the purse again and follows close to
see some piece of their service. Among a company of
seemly men was this lusty companion and his minion
gotten where both they might best behold the play, and
work for advantage; and ever this young nip was next to
him to mark when he should attempt any exploit, standing as it were more than half between the cunning nip
and his drab, only to learn some part of their skill.

In short time the deed was performed, but how, the
young nip could not easily discern. Only he felt him shift

41

his hand toward his trug, to convey the purse to her, but she, being somewhat mindful of the play, because a merriment was then upon the stage, gave no regard, whereby, thinking he had pulled her by the coat, he twitched the young nip by the cloak who, taking advantage of this offer, put down his hand and received the purse of him. Then counting it discourtesy to let him lose all his labour, he softly plucked the quean by the coat which she feeling, and imagining it had been her companion's hand received of him the first purse with the white counters in it. Then fearing lest his stay should hinder him, and seeing the other intended to have more purses ere he departed, away goes the young nip with the purse he got so easily, wherein as I have heard was thirty-seven shillings and odd money, which did so much content him as that he had beguiled so ancient a stander in that profession.

What the other thought when he found the purse and could not guess how he was cozened, I leave to your censures. Only this makes me smile: that one false knave can beguile another, which bids honest men look the better to their purses.

THE THIRD AND LAST PART OF CONNY-CATCHING

A Quaint Conceit of a Cutler and a Cutpurse
A nip [cutpurse] having by fortune lost his cuttle-bung [knife], or having not one fit for his purpose, went to a cunning cutler to have a new made, and prescribed the cutler such a method and form to make his knife, and the fashion to be strong, giving such a charge of the fineness of the temper and setting of the edge, that the cutler wondered what the gentleman would do with it. Yet, because he offered so largely for the making of it, the cutler was silent and made few questions, only he appointed the time to come for it, and that was three days later.

Well, the time being expired, the gentleman-nip came and, seeing the knife, liked it passing well, and gave him his money with advantage. The cutler desirous to know to what use he would put it, said to the cutpurse thus: 'Sir,' quoth he, 'I have made many knives in my days, and yet I never saw any of this form, fashion, temper, or edge, and therefore, if, without offence, I pray you tell me how or to what will you use it?'

While thus he stood talking with the nip, he, spying the purse in his apron, had cut it passing cunningly, and then, having his purchase close in his hand, made answer: 'In faith, my friend, to dissemble is a folly. 'Tis to cut a purse withal.'

'You are a merry gentleman,' quoth the cutler.

'I tell true,' quoth the cutpurse, and away he goes.

No sooner was he gone from the stall but there came another and bought a knife, and should have single money again. The cutler, thinking to put his hand in his bag, thrust it quite through at the bottom. All his money was gone, and the purse cut: 'Now I see! He that makes a snare, first falls into it himself. I made a knife to cut other mens' purses, and mine is the first. Well, revenge is fallen upon me, but I hope the rope will fall upon him!'

And so smoothed up the matter to himself, lest men should laugh at his strange fortune.

THE SECOND PART OF CONNY-CATCHING

A tradesman's wife of the Exchange, one day when her husband was following some business in the city, desired him he would give her leave to go see a play, which she had not done in seven years. He bade her take his apprentice along with her, and go, but especially to have a care of her purse, which she warranted him she would.

Sitting in a box, among some gallants and gallant

wenches, and returning when the play was done, returned
to her husband and told him she had lost her purse.
'Wife,' (quoth he), 'did I not give you warning of it?
How much money was there in it?'

Quoth she, 'Truly, four pieces, six shillings and a silver
toothpicker.'

Quoth her husband, 'Where did you put it?'

'Under my petticoat, between that and my smock.'

'What!' (quoth he), 'did you feel no body's hand
there?'

'Yes,' (quoth she), 'I felt one's hand there, but I did
not think he had come for that.'

THE ART OF LIVING IN LONDON

Gallant behaviour at the theatre

By sitting on the stage you may (with small cost), purchase the dear acquaintance of the boys, have a good
stool for sixpence, at any time know what particular part
any of the infants present, get your match lighted, examine the playsuits lace. Though the scarecrows in the yard
hoot at you, hiss at you, spit at you, yea throw dirt even
in your teeth – tis most Gentleman-like patience to
endure all this, and to laugh at the silly animals.

Before the play begins, fall to cards. You may win or
lose (as fencers do in a prize), and beat one another by
confederacy, yet share the money when you meet at
supper notwithstanding; to gull the ragamuffins that
stand aloof gaping at you, throw the cards (having first
torn four or five of them) round about the stage just upon
the third sound [of the theatre's trumpet] as though you
had lost. It skills not if four knaves lie on their backs,
and outface the audience, there's none such fools as dare
take exceptions at them, because ere the play go off,
better knaves than they will fall into the company.

Now, sir, if the writer be a fellow that hath either epigrammed you, or hath had a flirt at your mistress, or hath brought either your feather or your red beard, or your little legs etc. on the stage, you shall disgrace him worse than by tossing him in a blanket if, in the middle of his play (be it Pastoral or Comedy, Moral or Tragedy) you rise with a screwed and discontented face from your stool to be gone. No matter whether the scenes be good or no, the better they are the worse do you distaste them: and being on your feet, sneak not away like a coward, but salute all your gentle acquaintance, that are spread either on the rushes, or on stools about you, and draw what troop you can from the stage after you. The Mimicks are beholden to you for allowing them elbow room, their Poet cries perhaps, 'A pox go with you!' But care not you for that – there's no music without frets.

THE GULS HORNE-BOOKE

A Gentleman and a Drawer

A Gentleman crossed by a Drawer and conducted into a room two-pair of stairs high, thought thus to be revenged on him.

First, he knocks for the fellow, and bids him draw him a pint of wine. 'I will, I will sir,' answered the Drawer; but before he was at the lowest step of the first pair of stairs, he knocks again aloud for the Drawer, who answered, 'Anon, anon sir', but came up presently, and asked him what he would have.

'Drawer,' saith he, 'with the pint of wine bring me a chamber-pot.'

The Drawer ran down very nimbly, but the Gentleman knocked the third time, louder than he did before, insomuch that he was forced to come up again, and entering the room very angrily, asked him what he

45

wanted.

'Nothing,' saith the Gentleman, 'but this: I called thee first up, to bring me a chamber-pot, and now I would entreat thee, that thou wouldst not bring the wine up in the chamber-pot. '

A BANQUET OF JESTS

A certain conceyted traveller being at a banquet, where chanced a fly to fall into the cup, which he (being to drink) took out for himself, and afterwards put in again for his fellow: being demanded his reason, answered, that for his own part he affected them not, but it might be some other did!

CERTAYNE CONCEYTS AND JEASTS

Of a Horse and a Pecke of Oysters
A Gentleman, having rid hard in a wet morning and coming into his Inn dropping dry, saw a good fire in the Hall, but set so round that he could not get so much as shoulder room; for the weather being wet and cold, no man would give him place.

He, having espied oysters at the Inn gate, called in great haste to the Ostler to give his horse instantly a peck of oysters, for he purposed to ride away before dinner.

The Ostler was amazed, the rest wondered, but he would not rest till he saw them measured and cast before his horse into the manger. Strange it was to them all to hear of a horse that would eat oysters, and to behold the novelty they left presently the fire, and ran into the stable.

In the interim, the Gentleman warms and dries himself thoroughly from top to toe, at his pleasure. But they, gaping like fools some half an hour, came back again and told him his horse would not touch an oyster. 'No!' (saith he), 'Will not the sullen jade fall to? Well Ostler, bring 'em to me, and see what I can do with 'em: and (do you hear?), give my horse so many oats. '

Which, being done accordingly, by that time the horse had made an end of his oats, he had eaten his oysters, and the weather grew fair, and he, well dried, rode on his journey.

A BANQUET OF JESTS

A cheater having stolen a cup out of a Tavern, and being pursued in the streets, there grew on the sudden a great tumult of people, and a great confluence was gathered together. A civil Gentleman passing by, and seeing another come from thence that had been at the uproar, demanded of him what was the reason of that throng.

'Nothing,' saith he, 'but that one hath gotten a cup too much.'

'Alas,' saith the other, 'nothing else? That may be an honest man's fault, and mine as soon as an others!'

A BANQUET OF JESTS

Three Surgeons

Three Surgeons in their own countries were equally famous, and all at one time, the one in England, another in Ireland, a third in Wales. Now, as all men naturally enquire after such as are eminent in their own quality, so each of these by rumour having heard much of the others' excellency, they had great desire to see one another and were all in the same thought. The Irishman comes over to enquire after both, or either, just when the Englishman was journeying towards Wales, and the Welchman towards England.

These three by accident meet in one Inn, all strangers one to another. Motion was made by the Hostess, in regard they were single men, that they might sup togeth-

er; it was accepted of. After supper they grew in discourse of their own art. The Irishman extols one famous
in England, another in Wales. The Welchman is as lib-
eral in the praise of an Englishman and an Irishman. The
Englishman is as free in commending the other. After
some circumstance, they find themselves to be the same.

Many interchanges of courtesy passed between them
and, the table being drawn they concluded all to lie in
one chamber. A great fire being made, and some healths
passing round. At length saith the Englishman, 'We are
all famous for our art practised upon others; being so for-
tunately met it were not much amiss if we practised
something upon ourselves!' The others, as ambitious to
make trial of their skill, gave consent to the motion.

The Englishman presently calls for a clean, wooden
dish, and having commanded the Hostess to leave the
chamber, takes his incision knife and opens himself
before the fire, rips up his belly, takes out his stomach or
paunch and casts it into the wooden dish. Then binds up
his body, as his art taught him, without any trouble of
colour or countenance. Which they seeing, notwithstanding, cheered him up, and asked how he did. He
answered, 'I thank God, never better,' only for the
present he wanted a stomach. They applaud his cunning.

Then the Irishman loth to be exceeded in his art, with
his knife takes out one of his eyes, with the strings, and
without shew of fear or sign of pain closeth up the place
with a plaster and lays it to the Englishman's paunch in
the wooden platter.

Which the Welchman observing and scorning to be
undervalued in his art, leaps to his sword and takes it in
the left hand and cuts off the right, stauncheth the blood,
binds up the wound and casts it to the rest, as little
moved as the other. This done, they deliver up the

paunch, the eye, and the hand to be kept safe and delivered back to them in the morning. And then to bed they go.

The Hostess lays these things in the wet-larder, but her daughter forgetting to lock the door, about break of day, in comes a sow and eats up all in the tray.

The Hostess rising betimes in the morning, going to see her charge, finds all devoured, and no sign of anything remaining she grows into a great perplexity for her guests, grieving that she should be the cause of their deaths. Which her daughter over-hearing, comforts her mother thus. 'To satisfy your guests in show, and to avoid the law we have incurr'd by our negligence – first for the Englishman: they say the paunch of a hog, or a sow, is just like the stomach of a man or woman. Our sow is fat and to be killed shortly; cut her throat now, her flesh will never be a whit the worse, and lay her paunch in the place of the other.'

This was no sooner advised then put in practice. 'But now,' saith the Hostess, 'how shall we do for the Irishman's eye?'

'Oh Mother,' saith the girl, 'look but upon our grey-eyed cat, and she hath such eyes as he hath, for all the world.'

The mother apprehends, the cat is taken and suffers, and her eye cast into the tray instead of the Irishman's.

That done, 'What shift,' (saith mine Hostess), 'shall we make for the Welchman's hand?'

'Oh Mother,' saith the girl, 'but yesterday a thief suffered, and hangs still upon the gallows. Send quickly to the place and cut off his hand, and lay it in the place of the Welchman's.'

All is done. The Surgeons call. The tray is carried up and (as they think) everything accommodated in his own place. The Englishman closeth up his stomach, the Irishman puts in his eye, the Welchman fastens on his hand, and every of them in outward appearance seems whole and sound. And being ready to take horse and part, saith one of them, 'The cures seem current for the present but whether they be settled, or permanent, may be a question. Therefore, I hold it fit that every one of us travel about our most necessary affairs and meet here again in the same place, this day month, to give account of our cures.' It is concluded.

The day comes. The artists appear, according to promise. They first ask the Englishman concerning the state of his body, who answered he was never in better health, nor ever had so great a stomach. For now, no meat can come amiss to him, raw or roasted. Besides, he had much ado to keep his nose out of every swilling-tub. Nay, he cannot see a young child turn his back-side to the wall, but he had a great mind to be doing with it!

They question the Irishman of his health, who answers that he feels himself well, saving that he feels some defect in that one eye; for when the one is shut and asleep, the other is open and awake. Besides, if at midnight he hear a rat or mouse stirring, he could not contain himself from stepping out of bed, breaking his shin so often that they are never without plasters!

They question the Welchman last. He protests that he is well, and in health, and that in his own nature he is both of good condition and conversation; but ever since the rejoining of that hand, he hath much ado from stealing whatsoever stands in his way, and keeping it out of the next man's pocket!

A BANQUET OF JESTS

How Tarlton tooke tobacco at the first comming up of it
Tarlton, as other gentlemen used, at the first coming up
of tobacco, did take it more for fashion's sake than other
wise; and being in a room set between two men overcome
with wine, and they never seeing the like, wondered at it;
and seeing the vapour come out of Tarlton's nose, cried
out: 'Fire, fire!' and threw a cup of wine in Tarlton's face.

'Make no more stir,' quoth Tarlton, 'the fire is
quenched; if the sheriffs come, it will turn to a fine, as
the custom is.'

And drinking that again: 'Fie,' says the other, 'what a
stink it makes; I am almost poisoned.'

'If it offend,' says Tarlton, 'let's every one take a little
of the smell, and so the savour will quickly go.'

But tobacco whiffs made them leave him to pay all.

TARLTONS JESTS

Tarlton jest of a country wench
Tarlton, going towards Hogsdon, met a country maid
coming to market; her mare stumbling, down she fell
over and over, showing all: and then rising up again, she
turned her round about unto Master Tarlton, and said:
'God's body, sir, did you ever see the like before?'

'No, in good sooth,' quoth Tarlton, 'never but once, in
London.'

TARLTONS JESTS

How a maid drave Tarlton to a Non-plus
Tarlton meeting with a witty country wench, who gave
him quip for quip:

'Sweet heart,' (said he), 'would my flesh were in
thine.'

'So would I, sir,' (says she), 'I would your nose were in
my, I know where!'

51

Tarlton angered at this, said no more, but goes forward.

TARLTONS JESTS

A man being deeply in play at dice, having lost much money, his son (a little lad) being by him wept. Quoth the father: 'Boy, why dost thou weep?'

The boy answered, that he had read that Alexander the Great wept when he heard that his father (King Philip) had conquered many Cities, Towns, and Territories, fearing that he would leave him nothing to win; 'And I weep the contrary way,' (quoth the boy), 'for I fear that my father will leave me nothing to lose!'

TAYLORS WIT AND MIRTH

The Vincent's Law, with the Discovery Thereof
The vincent's law is a common deceit or cozenage used in bowling alleys, amongst the baser sort of people who commonly haunt such lewd and unlawful places. For although I will not discommend altogether the nature of bowling if the time, place, person, and such necessary circumstances be observed, yet as it is now used, practised and suffered it groweth altogether to the maintenance of unthrifts, that idly and disorderly make that recreation a cozenage.

Now the manner and form of their device is thus effected: the bawkers, for so the common haunters of the alley are termed, apparelled like very honest and substantial citizens come to bowl, as though rather they did it for sport than gains, and under that colour of carelessness, do shadow their pretended knavery. Well, to bowls they go and then there resort of all sorts of people to behold them. Some simple men brought in of purpose by some cozening companions to be stripped of his crowns, others, gentlemen, or merchants, that delighted with the sport, stand there as beholders to pass away the time.

Amongst these are certain old sokers, which are lookers on, and listen for bets, either even or odd, and these are called gripes. And these fellows will refuse no lay, if the odds may grow to their advantage, for the gripes and the bawkers are confederate, and their fortune at play ever sorts according as the gripes have placed their bets. For the bawker, he marketh how the lays goes, and so throws his casting, so that (note this), the bowlers cast ever booty, and doth win or lose as the bet of the gripe leadeth them. For suppose seven be up for the game, and the one hath three and the other none, then the vincent, for that is the simple man that stands by, and not acquainted with their cozenage, nor doth so much as once imagine that the bawkers, that carry the countenance of honest substantial men, would by any means or for any gains, be persuaded to play booty.

Well, this vincent (for so the cozeners or gripes please to term him) seeing three to none, beginneth to offer odds on that side that is fairest to win . . . . Now, to shadow the matter the more, the bawker that wins and is afore-hand with the game, will lay frankly that he shall win, and will bet hard, and lay great odds – but with whom? Either with them which play with him, that are as crafty knaves as himself, or else with the gripe, and this makes the vincent stoop to the blow, and to lose all the money in his purse.

Besides, if any honest men that hold themselves skilful in bowling, offer to play any set match against these common bawkers, if they fear to have the worse, or suspect the others play to be better than theirs, then they have a trick in watering of the alley to give such a moisture to the bank that he offers to strike a bowl with a shore, shall never hit it whilst he lives, because the moisture of the bank hinders the proportion of his aiming.

Divers other practices there are in bowling tending unto cozenage, but the greatest is booty, and therefore would I wish all men that are careful of their coin, to beware of such cozeners and none to come in such places, where a haunt of such hellrakers are resident, and not in any wise stoop to their bets, lest he be made a vincent . . . Seeing then as the game is abused to a deceit, that is made for an honest recreation, let this be a caveat for men to have an insight into their knavery.

THE SECOND PART OF CONNY-CATCHING

Pedlers French

Here I set before thee (good Reader) the lewd lousy language of these loitering lusks and lazy lorels, wherewith they buy and sell the common people as they pass through the country. Which language they term 'Pedlers French', an unknown tongue to all but these bold beastly bawdy beggars and vain vagabonds, being half mingled with English when it is familiarly talked, and first placing things by their proper names, as an introduction to this peevish speech.

Nab, a head
Nabchet, a hat or cap
Glassers, eyes
Gan, a mouth
Fambles, hands
Prat, a buttock
Stamps, legs
Togman, a coat
Drawers, hose
Stampers, shoes
Duddes, clothes
Bung, a purse
Lowre, money
Boose, drink
stow you, hold your peace
to cant, to speak

Bene, good
Pannam, bread
Pek, meat
Patrico, a priest
Nosegent, a nun
a Ken, a house
a Stauling ken, a house that will receive stolen ware
a Boosing ken, an alehouse
lage, water
Rome-vill, London
Romeboose, wine
a gentry cove, a gentleman
filch, to steal
To nip a bung, to cut a purse
to niggle, to have to do with a woman carnally

The manner of their canting speache
By this little you may wholly and fully understand their
untoward talk and pelting speech, mingled without mea-
sure . . . .

Bene lightmans to thy quarroms.
Good morrow to thy body.

Hast thou any lowre in thy bung to boose?
Hast thou any money in thy purse to drink?

Why where is the ken that hath bene boose?
Where is the house that hath the good drink?

*Tower ye, yonder is the ken, dup the gigger and maund
that is beneship.*
See you. Yonder is the house. Open the door and ask
for the best.

This is as good as Rome boose.
This drink is as good as wine.

Now I tower that bene boose makes nase nabs.
Now I see that good drink makes a drunken head.

Maund of this morte what bene pecke is in her ken.
Ask of this wife what good meat she hath in her
house.

Now we have well boosed let us strike some chete.
Now we have well drunk let us steal something.

*So may we happen on the harmans, and clye the jark, or to
the queerken, and skower queer crampings, and so to try*

on the chats.
So we may chance to sit in the stocks, or be whipped, or had to prison house, and there be shackled with bolts and fetters, and then to hang on the gallows.

Gerry gan the ruffian clye thee.
A turd in thy mouth the Devil take thee.

What, stow you bene cove and cut benar whydds, and bing we to Rome-vill to nip a bung, so shall we have lowre for the boosing ken, and when we bing back to the deuse-vill we will filch some duddes of the ruffmans or mill the ken for a lag of duddes.

What, hold your peace good fellow and speak better words, and go we to London to cut a purse, then we shall have money for the alehouse, and when we come back again into the country, we will steal some linen clothes off hedges, or rob some house for a buck of clothes.

A CAVEAT OR WARNING FOR COMMEN CURSETORS

Of the traveller returned from Italy
Italy, the paradise of the earth and the epicure's heaven, how doth it form our young master? It makes him to kiss his hand like an ape, cringe his neck like a starveling, and play at 'heypass, repass come aloft', when he salutes a man.

From thence he brings the art of atheism, the art of epicurising, the art of whoring, the art of poisoning, the art of sodomitry. The only probable good thing they have to keep us from utterly condemning it is that it maketh a man an excellent courtier, a curious carpet knight, which is, by interpretation, a fine close lecher, a glorious hypocrite.

It is now a privy note amongst the better sort of men,

when they would set a singular mark or brand on a notorious villain, to say : he hath been in Italy.

THE UNFORTUNATE TRAVELLER

*How a young Italian merchant, one Master Benedick, coming
to Jack of Newbury's house, was greatly enamoured of his
kinswoman Joan, and how he was served*

'O dissembling Italian!' quoth Jack. 'I will be revenged
on him for this wrong!

I know that any favour from Joan my kinswoman will
make him run like a man bitten with a mad dog.
Therefore, thou shalt see me dress him in his kind. To
supper will I invite Joan my kinswoman, and in the mean
space make up the bed in the parlour very decently.'

So the good man went forth, and got a sleepy drench
from the pothecary's, the which he gave to a young sow
which he had in his yard, and in that evening laid her
down in the bed in the parlour, drawing the curtains
round about.

Supper time being come, Master Benedick gave his
attendance, glad of Mistress Joan's company, passed the
supper time with many pleasant conceits, Joan showing
herself that night more pleasant in his company than at
any time before; therefore he gave the good man great
thanks.

'Good Master Benedick,' (quoth Jack), 'little do you
think how I have travailed in your behalf to my
kinswoman, and much ado I had to bring the peevish
wench into any good liking of your love. Notwithstanding, by my great diligence and persuasions I did at
length win her good will to come hither, little thinking
to find you here, or any such good cheer to entertain her,
all which I see is fallen out for your profit. But trust me,
all the world cannot alter her mind, nor turn her love

from you. In regard whereof, she hath promised me to lie
this night in my house for the great desire she hath of
your good company, and in requital of all your great cour-
tesies showed to me, I am very well content to bring you
to her bed. Marry this you must consider, and so she
bade me tell you: that you should come to bed with as little noise as you could, and tumble nothing that you find,
for fear of her best gown and her hat, which she will lay
hard by the bedside next her best partlet [ruff], and in so
doing you may have company with her all night; but say
nothing in any case till you be abed.'

Master Benedick thought every hour twain till the sun
was down, and that he were abed with his beloved. At
last he had his wish . . . . Then said Jack : 'Master
Benedick, you must not in any case have a candle when
you go into the chamber, for then my kinswoman will be
angry, and dark places fit best lovers' desires.'

'O Master Jak,' quoth he, ' 'tis no such matter for light;
me shall find Metress Joan will enough in the dark.' And
entering in the parlour, groping about, he felt a gown and
a hat. 'O Metress Joan,' quoth he, 'here is your gown and
hat. Me shall no hurt for a tousand pound.'

Then kneeling down by the bed's side, instead of
Mistress Joan he saluted the sow in this sort: 'O my love
and my delight, it is thy fair face that hath wounded my
heart; thy grey sparkling eyes and thy lily-white hands,
with the comely proportion of thy pretty body, that made
me in seeking thee to forget myself and, to find thy
favour, lose my own feedom. But now is the time come
wherein I shall reap the fruits of a plentiful harvest.

Now, my dear, from thy sweet mouth let me suck the
honey balm of thy breath, and with my hand stroke those
rosy cheeks of thine wherein I have took such pleasure.
Come with thy pretty lips and entertain me into thy bed

with one gentle kiss (why speakest thou not, my sweet-heart?) and stretch out thy alabaster arms to enfold thy faithful friend. Why should ill-pleasing sleep close up the crystal windows of thy body so fast and bereave thee of thy fine, lordly attendants wherewith thou wast wont to salute thy friends?

Let it not offend thy gentle ears that I thus talk to thee. If thou hast vowed not to speak I will not break it, and if thou wilt command me to be silent I will be dumb. But thou needest not fear to speak thy mind, seeing the cloudy night concealeth everything.'

By this time Master Benedick was unready, and slipped into bed, where the sow lay swathed in a sheet and her head bound in a great linen cloth. As soon as he was laid, he began to embrace his new bedfellow, and laying his lips somewhat near her snout, he felt her draw her breath very short. 'Why, how now love,' quoth he, 'be you sick? Mistress Joan, your breath be very strong; have you no cacke abed?'

The sow, feeling herself disturbed, began to grunt and keep a great stir, whereat Master Benedick, like a mad-man, ran out of bed crying, 'De divel, de divel!'

The good man of the house, being purposely provided, came rushing in with half a dozen neighbours, asking what was the matter. 'Poh me!' quoth Benedick, 'here be the great divel, cry "hoh, hoh, hoh" – be Gossen I tink dee play the knave vid me, and me will be revenged on you!'

'Walk! walk! Berkshire maids will be no Italian's strumpets!' the good man and his neighbours laughed aloud; away went Master Benedick, and for very shame departed from Newbury before day.

JACK OF NEWBURY

Of the traveller returned from Spain

From Spain what bringeth our traveller? A skull-crowned hat of the fashion of an old deep porringer, a diminutive alderman's ruff with short strings like the droppings of a man's nose, a close-bellied doublet coming down with a peak behind as far as the crupper and cut off before by the breast-bone like a partlet or neckercher, a wide pair of gaskins which ungathered would make a couple of women's riding-kirtles, huge hangers that have half a cow-hide in them, a rapier that is lineally descended from half a dozen dukes at the least.

He jetteth strutting, dancing on his toes with his hands under his sides. If you talk to him, he makes a dishcloth of his own country in comparison of Spain, but if you urge him more particularly wherein it exceed, he can give no instance but in Spain they have better bread than we have.

THE UNFORTUNATE TRAVELLER

A Spaniard travelling from Dover towards London, being benighted was forced to knock at a poor Alehouse for lodging. The Hostess demanding his name, he told her it was : Don Pedro Gonzales Gaietan de Gueveza. To whom the good woman answered, 'Alas sir, my small house neither affords room nor meat for so many!'

A BANQUET OF JESTS

Of the traveller returned from France
What is there in France to be learned more than in England but falsehood in fellowship, perfect slovenry, to love no man but for my pleasure, to swear, 'Ah par la mort Dieu,' when a man's hams are scabbed?

I have known some that have continued there by the space of half a dozen year, and when they come home they have hid a little wearish face under a broad French hat, kept a terrible coil with the dust in the street in their long cloaks of grey paper, and spoke English strangely.

Nought else have they profited by their travel save learnt to distinguish of the true Bordeaux grape, and know a cup of neat Gascoigne wine from wine of Orleance. Yea, and peradventure, this also: to esteem of the pox as a pimple, to wear a velvet patch on their face, and walk melancholy with their arms folded.

THE UNFORTUNATE TRAVELLER

The Gulling of a Gallant

I will tell you: thus it was I being in my youth reasonably well favoured, of a pure complexion, and of a reasonable good nature, and having wit enough, upon a little warning to play the wag in the right vein, it was my hap among other my fellow pages, to take knowledge of a certain gallant in our Court, a man of no great worth any way, and yet a sufficient block for frogs to leap upon.

His years about some twenty two or thereabouts . . . a most wicked face, and a wit correspondent: to be short, for that ill faces makes no pleasant descriptions, let it suffice, that he was every way a very filthy fellow, and yet having better clothes than he was worthy to wear, and more money than he could wisely use, this Lob-lillie, with slavering lips, would be making love, and that not only to one, but every day one and though he were scarce welcome to any, yet would he blush at no disgrace. We devised to lay a plot to befool him to the full.

We had among us one fine boy (I will not say myself) whose feature and beauty made him an amiable creature. This youth, we had agreed among ourselves, to make a means by which to catch this wood-cock in a fine springe: which in few days after, we enacted, as I will tell you. We got apparrel of a Gentle-woman, (a waiting woman of a Lady) of whom, having acquainted her with our intended sport, we borrowed many things fit for our purpose. This boy (being now a supposed wench) we caused to take a lodging where out of his window, beholding this beautiful object, his eyes were no sooner limed with blindness, but his heart was so set on fire with folly, that there was no way to quench it, but the favour of this imagined fair Lady, Gentle-woman, or mistress, what you will.

Now, we that daily used to visit him, no sooner in his

chamber having gotten a view of her, but we fell with admiration to commend her beyond the moon for an excellent creature – Oh, what an eye! what a lip! what a forehead! what a cheek! what a hair! what a hand! what a body! – for further, at the window, we could not see. Thus, little by little, we brought him half mad before with conceit, ready to hang himself for love. And now must those little wits we had, go to work to shew his folly.

Now we must get him a poet, to make him verses in her commendation, a scholar to write his love letters, music to play under her window and gloves, scarves, and fans to be sent for presents, which might be, as it were, fore-speakers for his entertainment. And thus, when we had fitted him for all turns, we got him such favourable access upon promise of no dishonourable attempt that, where before he was but overshoes, he was now over-head-and-ears for an ass.

Well, thus having a few days played with his nose, and having agreed with them of the house to seem ignorant of her name and country but that she was a suitor at the Court, they knew not wherefore when in pity to pull the poor fool too low on his knees, with holding him off too long from his off or on.

We devised one night that he should be at great cost with a supper in her lodging, and there should be certain Gentle-women to accompany her and that should offer her what kindness might lie in their powers in the Court. These we brought, as we made him believe, to let them see his favour and good regard with this rare creature, but came indeed only with a forced modesty, to conceal a laughing at this coxcomb.

Not to dwell too long upon circumstances, the supper was provided, the guests bidden, the music in tune, the Gentleman welcome, and the boy played his part. He

had the kiss of the hand, vows and
protestations, gifts and presents,
and what not, that might witness of his folly. Now a
little before supper understanding (by the imagined wench)
that she was the next morning to go
out of town, after solemn promise to
bring her on her way (kindly accepted
on her part) to supper they went,
where there were so many healths
drunk to his mistress, that with as
much ado as might be drunken to save
his credit he took his leave till morning, and so got him
home to his lodging; where, having scarce power to stand
on his feet, he fell down on his bed, where with the help
of a little trick that was put in a cup of wine, he slept till
next day noon, when like a great bear grunting and blow-
ing he goeth to the window, where missing his former
object (who had now turned Page again), ashamed of his
breach of promise, got him to bed again, where keeping
his chamber for a day or two, and then coming into the
Court, seeing some of his favours worn by one of the
Pages, the boy that played the wag with him.

Ashamed to demand them, and fearing his folly to be
known in Court, he suddenly turned Clown, and with a
sighing song, to the tune of *Wela day, wel adaie* got him
in to the country, where we never heard more of him.
Now sir, was not this a pretty jest, and well handled?

GRIMELLO'S FORTUNES

A Tale of Jemy Camber

There was a Laundress of the town, whose daughter used often to the Court to bring home shirts and bands, which Jemy had long time loved and solicited, but to no end. She would not yield him an inch of her maidenhead. Now Jemy vowed he would have it all.

Well, she consented at last and to be short soon at night at nine a clock, being in the winter, when she knew her mother to be gone to watch with a sick body, he should come and all that night lie with her. Jemy though witless, wanted no knavish meaning in this, thought long till it was night. But in the afternoon, this maid goes up to the castle and gathers a great basket of nettles, and coming home strews them under the bed.

Night comes, nine a clock strikes, Jemy on his horse comes riding forward, sets him up and knocks at the door; she lets him in and bids him welcome, bonny man. To bed he goes, and Jemy ever used to lie naked, as is the use of a number amongst which number she knew Jemy was one, who no sooner was in bed, but she herself knocked at the door, and herself asked who was there, which Jemy, hearing was afraid of her mother.

'Alas, sir!' (says she), 'creep under the bed, my mother comes.'

Jemy bustled not a little, under he creeps stark naked, where he was stung with nettles. Judge you that have feeling of such matters: there he lay turning this way and that way; here he stung his leg, here his shoulder, there his buttocks: but the maid having locked the door to him, went to bed and there lay he in durance (as they say) till morning.

When the day broke up gets the maid, to Court she goes, and tells the King's Chamberlain of the matter, and he told the King, who laughed thereat right heartily.

A NEST OF NINNIES

Elizabethan Humour

A Company at Dinner

A sudden silence being at a table where many guests were sitting at dinner, one amongst them said aloud, 'Why, how now Gentlemen and Gentlewomen? How comes it to pass that there is not one word amongst us all? I am afraid that some of you sit cross-legg'd.'

A young Gentlewoman looking up in his face, replied, 'It is not I sir, I assure you: for I have something betwixt my legs' . . . meaning the trestle of the table.

A BANQUET OF JESTS

A common wench stepping into a boat fell into the water, and reaching her hand to be helped out, one refused it, saying she need not fear drowning, for she was so light, she could never sink.

CONCEITS, CLINCHES, FLASHES AND WHIMZIES

To knowe if a Woman be with a man child or not

Take a dish and put water in it, and then let her milk her breast into the water, and if it be a man child, it will float, and if it be a woman child it will sink.

A BRIEFE TREATISE OF NATURALL & ARTIFICIALL CONCLUSIONS

Tis probable that those women that 'paint' most shall live longest; for where a house is kept in repair, there is no fear but it will be inhabited.

CONCEITS, CLINCHES, FLASHES AND WHIMZIES

*Of hym that warned his wife of wasshynge her face in foule
puddell water*

A man dwelling in the country, taking his journey, bade
his wife in his absence play the good housewife, that he
at his home-coming might find all things well.

'Sweet husband,' (quoth she), 'command what ye will,
and you shall find me obedience in all things.'

'Dear heart,' (said he), 'I will you no more but this one
thing, which is easy enough to do.'

'What is that?' (quoth she).

'That you wash not your face with this water,' showing
her a puddle in a dunghill, foul black, and stinking.

As oft as she in his absence went by that puddle, her
mind was marvellously moved, for what cause her husband so diligently warned her of that thing only. Nor she
could not persuade herself, but that there was some great
thing in it. To be brief, it tempted her so, that she
washed, that is, she defiled her face. She looked in the
glass, and was greatly displeased with her self. Yea, it was
four or five days after, ere she could wash out the stink
and staining.

When the good man came home, he found his wife
very pensive and looking angerly. 'What is the matter?'
(quoth he). She at last could not forbear, but blamed
him for warning her not to wash in that water, and
showed him what had chanced.

'Why washed you in it?' (quoth he). 'I gave you warning, that you not wash therein, to the intent this harm
should not have happened!'

By this tale ye may perceive, that the more you forbid
some women a thing, the greater desire they have to do
it.

MERY TALES, WITTIE QUESTIONS, AND QUICKE
ANSWERES

How Jack of Newbury's servants were revenged on a tattling gossip

Now, certain of the maidens of the house and some of the young men, who had long before determined to be revenged of this prattling housewife, came into the cellar one after another, one of them bringing a great piece of a gambon of bacon in his hand, and everyone bade Mistress Frank welcome. And first one drank to her, and then another, and so the third, the fourth, and the fifth, so that Mistress Frank's brains waxed as mellow as a pippin at Michaelmas, and so light that, sitting in the cellar, she thought the world ran round. They, seeing her fall into merry humours, whetted her on in merriment as much as they could, saying, 'Mistress Frank spare not I pray you, but think yourself as welcome as any woman in Newbury, for we have cause to love you because you love our mistress so well.'

'Now, assure you,' quoth she, lisping in her speech, her tongue waxing somewhat big for her mouth, 'I love your mistress well indeed, as if she were my own daughter.'

'Nay, but hear you,' quoth they, 'she begins not to deal well with us now.'

'No, my lamb?' quoth she, 'Why so?'

'Because,' quoth they, 'she seeks to bar us of our allowance, telling our master that he spends too much in housekeeping.'

'Nay, then,' quoth she, 'your mistress is an ass and a fool, and though she go in her hood, what care I? She is but a girl to me. Twittle twattle, I know what I know. Go to, drink to me. Well Tweedle, I drink to thee with all my heart; why thou whoreson, when wilt thou be married? O that I were a young wench for thy sake. But 'tis no matter . . . and your mistress now she is rich and I am

69

poor, but 'tis no matter, I knew her a draggle-tail girl, mark ye.'

'But now,' quoth they, 'she takes upon her lustily and hath forgot what she was.'

'Tush, what will you have of a green thing?' quoth she, 'Here, I drink to you. So long as she goes where she list a-gossiping; and 'tis no matter, little said is soon amended. But hear you, my masters, though Mistress Winchcomb go in her hood, I am as good as she, I care not who tell it her. Go to, go to, I know what I say well enough. I am sure I am not drunk. Mistress Winchcomb – Mistress? No, Nan Winchcomb I will call her name, plain Nan. What? I was a woman when she was, se-reverence, a paltry girl, though now she goes in her hood and chain of gold. What care I for her? I am her elder, and I know more of her tricks. Nay, I warrant you I know what I say, 'tis no matter, laugh at me and spare not. I am not drunk I warrant.'

And with that, being scant able to hold open her eyes, she began to nod and to spill the wine out of her glass, which they perceiving let her alone, going out of the cellar till she was sound asleep, and in the mean space they devised how to finish this piece of knavery. At last they consented to lay her forth at the back side of the house, half a mile off, even at the foot of a stile, that whosoever came next over might find her. Notwithstanding, Tweedle stayed hard by to see the end of the action.

At last comes a notable clown from Greenham taking his way to Newbury who, coming hastily over the stile, stumbled at the woman and fell down clean over her. But in the starting up, seeing it was a woman, cried out, 'Alas, alas!'

'How now, what is the matter?' quoth Tweedle.

'O,' quoth he, 'here lies a dead woman.'

'A dead woman?' quoth Tweedle, 'that's not so I trow.'
And with that he tumbled her about. 'Bones of me!'
quoth Tweedle, 'it's a drunken woman, and one of the
town undoubtedly. Surely it is great pity she should lie
here.'

'Why, do you know her?' quoth the clown.

'No, not I,' quoth Tweedle, 'Nevertheless, I will give
thee half a groat, and take her in thy basket and carry her
throughout the town, and see if anybody know her.'

'Then,' said the other, 'let me see the money and I
will,' for by the mass he earned not half a groat this great
while.

'There it is,' quoth Tweedle.

Then the fellow put her in his basket and so lifted her
upon his back. 'Now by the mass, she stinks vilely of
drink or wine or something. But tell me, what shall I say
when I come into he town?' quoth he.

'First,' quoth Tweedle, 'I would have thee, so soon as

ever thou canst, go to the town's end with a lusty voice to cry, *O yes*, and then say, *Who knows this woman, who?* And though possible some will say I know her and I know her, yet do not thou set her down till thou comest to the market cross, and there use the like words; and if any be so friendly to tell thee where she dwells, then just before her door cry so again, and if thou perform this bravely I will give thee half a groat more.'

And so away he went till he came to the town's end, and there he cries out as boldly as any bailiff's man, 'O yes! Who knows this woman, who?'

Then said the drunken woman in the basket, her head falling first on one side and then on the other side; 'Who co me, who?'

Then he said again, 'Who knows this woman, who?'

'Who co me, who?' quoth she. And look; how oft he spake the one, she spake the other, saying still, 'Who co me, who co me, who?' Whereat all the people in the street fell into such a laughing that the tears ran down again.

At last one made answer saying, 'Good fellow, she dwells in the North-brook Street, a little beyond Master Winchcomb's.'

The fellow, hearing that, gets down thither in haste, and there in hearing of a hundred people cries, 'Who knows this woman, who?'

Whereat her husband comes out saying, 'Marry, that do I – too well, God help me.'

'Then,' said the clown, 'if you know her take her, for I know her not but for a drunken beast.'

And as her husband took her out of the basket, she gave him a sound box on the ears, saying, 'What you queans, do you mock me?' And so was carried in.

But the next day, when her brains were quiet and her

head cleared of these foggy vapours, she was so ashamed of herself that she went not forth of her doors a long time after, and if anybody did say unto her, 'Who co me, who?' she would be so mad and furious that she would be ready to draw her knife and to stick them, and scold as if she strove for the best game at the cucking stools.

JACK OF NEWBURY

The Seventh Tale of the Mad Men of Gottam
When the Good-Friday was come, the men of Gottam did cast their heads together what to do with their white herring, their red herring, their sprats and salt fish.

One consulted with the other, and agreed that such fish should be cast into their pond or pool (the which was in the middle of the town), that it might increase against the next year; and every man that had any fish left, did cast them into the pool.

The one said: 'I have thus many white herrings;' another said : 'I have thus many sprats;' another said : 'I have thus many red herrings;' and the other said : 'I have thus many salt fishes. Let all go together into the pool or pond, and we shall fare like lords the next Lent.'

At the beginning of the next Lent following, the men did draw the pond to have their fish, and there was nothing but a great eel.

'Ah,' said they all, 'a mischief on this eel, for he hath eaten up all our fish.'

'What shall we do with him?' said the one to the other.

'Kill him,' said the one of them.

'Chop him all to pieces,' said another.

'Nay, not so,' said the other, 'let us drown him.'

'Be it so,' said all.

They went to another pool or pond by, and did cast in

the eel into the water.

'Lie there,' said they, 'and shift for thyself; for no help thou shalt have of us.'

And there they left the eel to be drowned.

The Tenth Tale of the Mad Men of Gottam

On a certain time, there were twelve men of Gottam, that did go a fishing, and some did wade in the water, and some stood upon dry land, and when they went homeward, one said to the other: 'We have ventured wonderful hard this day in wading; I pray God, that none of us that did come from home be drowned.'

'Marry,' said the one to the other, 'let us see that, for there did twelve of us come out.'

And they told themselves, and every man did tell eleven, and the twelfth man did never tell himself.

'Alas,' said the one to the other, 'there is one of us drowned.'

They went back to the brook, where that they had been fishing, and sought up and down for him that was drowned, and did make great lamentation.

A Courtier did come riding by, and he did ask what it was they did seek, and why they were so sorry.

'O,' said they, 'this day we went to fish in this brook, and there did come out twelve of us, and one is drowned.'

'Why,' said the Courtier, 'what will you give me, and I will find out twelve men?'

'Sir,' said they, 'all the money that we have.'

'Give me the money,' said the Courtier: and he began with the first, and did give him a goodly blow over the shoulders that he groaned, and said: 'There is one.' So he served all, that they groaned on the matter.

When he did come to the last, he paid him a good, saying: 'Here is the twelfth man.'

'Gods blessing on your heart,' said all the company, 'that you have found out our neighbour.'

MERY TALES OF THE MAD MEN OF GOTTAM

How mad Coomes, when his wife was drowned, sought her against the streame

Coomes of Stapforth, hearing that his wife was drowned coming from market, went with certain of his friends to see if they could find her in the river. He, contrary to all the rest, sought his wife against the stream; which they perceiving, said he looked the wrong way.

'And why so?' (quoth he).

'Because,' (quoth they), 'you should look down stream and not against it.'

'Nay, zounds,' (quoth he), 'I shall never find her that way: for she did all things so contrary in her lifetime, that now she is dead, I am sure she will go against the stream.'

PASQUILS JESTS

A traveller reported to be drowned, a friend of his being in company when the letters came that brought the first news of his death, fetched a great sigh with these words – 'God rest his soul, for he is gone the way of all flesh.'

'Nay,' saith another, then standing by. 'If he be drowned, he is rather gone the way of all fish.'

A BANQUET OF JESTS

A Woman the Weaker Vessell
A cooper beat his wife with a hoop, for pissing her bed. When the neighbours, to reconcile him to her, told him she was the weaker vessel; 'Therefore,' (quoth he), 'do I hoop her, because she should hold water.'

A BANQUET OF JESTS

A Welsh man reading the chapter of the Genealogy where Abraham beget Isaac, and Isaac begat Jacob: ere he came to the midst he found the names so difficult that he broke off in these words: '. . . and so they begat one another, till they came to the end of the Chapter.'

A BANQUET OF JESTS

How Tarlton answered a wanton Gentlewoman
A Gentlewoman merrily disposed, being crossed by Tarlton, and half angry said, 'Sirra, a little thing would make me requite you with a cuff.'

'With a cuff, Lady?' says Tarlton. 'So would you spell my sorrow forward: but spell my sorrow *backward*, then cuff me and spare not!'

When the Gentlemen by considered of the word, they laughing, made the simple meaning Gentlewoman to blush for shame.

TARLTONS JESTS

A melancholy gentleman sitting one day at table started up on a sudden, and meaning to say, 'I must go buy a dagger,' by transposing of the letters said: 'I must go die a beggar!'

A BANQUET OF JESTS

One asked why B stood before C. Because, said another, a man must B before he can C.

CONCEITS, CLINCHES, FLASHES AND WHIMZIES

Queen Elizabeth and the Scholar

A worthy Gentleman and a good scholar had been long in disgrace with Queen Elizabeth – the reason I know not, nor am willing to examine – but he means to one that was in great favour in the court to bring him into favour with Her Majesty which he had promised him, and persuaded the Queen to give admittance of him into her presence.

The time was come, and the other brought him where and when she expected him. Who, having done his duty with all the submission that a subject might, the Queen saith, 'I understand you are a great scholar; shall I ask you one question?'

'Any thing, madam,' saith he, 'that lies within the compass of my understanding to resolve you.'

'Then, I pray you, how many *vowels* be there?'

'Madam,' saith he, 'it is a question that every school-boy can resolve you; but since you would be answered from me – there be five.'

'Five,' saith she, 'But I pray you, of these five, which may we best spare?'

'Not any of them, Madam,' saith he, 'without corrupting of our natural dialect.'

'Yes,' replied she, 'I can tell you; for of them all we can (for our own part) best spare U!'

A BANQUET OF JESTS

One asked which of the letters in the alphabet were the most authentic in a Bill or Bond. It was answered, I, O, U.

CONCEITS, CLINCHES FLASHES AND WHIMZIES

How the maidens served Will Summers for his sauciness
The King and Queen, laughing heartily, rose from the table, by which time Jack of Newbury had caused all his folks to go to their work, that his Grace and all the nobility might see it; so indeed the Queen had requested. Then came his Highness where he saw an hundred looms

standing in one room, and two men working in every one. His Majesty came next among the spinners and carders who were merrily a-working whereat Will Summers fell into a great laughter.

'What ails the fool to laugh?' said the King.

'Marry,' quoth Will Summers, 'to see these maidens get their living as bulls do eat their meat.'

'How is that?' said the Queen.

'By going still backward,' quoth Will Summers, 'and I will lay a wager that they that practise so well being maids to go backward will quickly learn ere long to fall backward!'

The King, Queen and nobles being ready to depart, after great thanks and gifts given to Jack of Newbury his majesty would have made him knight, but he meekly refused it.

But in this meanspace, Will Summers kept company among the maids, and betook himself to spinning as they did, which among them was held as a forfeit of a gallon of wine, but William by no means would pay it except they would take it out in kisses, rating every kiss at a farthing. 'This payment we refuse for two causes,' quoth the maidens, 'the one for that we esteem not kisses at so base a rate, and the other because in so doing we should give as much as you.'

The maidens consented together, seeing Will Summers was so busy both with his work and in his words, and would not pay his forfeiture, to serve him as he served.

First therefore, they bound him hand and foot, and set him upright against a post, tying him thereto – which he took in ill part, notwithstanding he could not resist them; and because he let his tongue run at random, they set a fair gag in his mouth, such a one as he could not for his life put away, so that he stood as one gaping for wind. Then one of them got a couple of dog's droppings and, putting them in a bag, laid them in soak in a basin of water, while the rest turned down the collar of his jerkin and put an house cloth about his neck instead of a fine towel. Then came the other maid with a basin and water in the same, and with the 'perfume' of her pudding bag flapped him about the face and lips till he looked like a tawny Moor, and with her hand washed him very orderly.

The smell being somewhat strong, Will could by no means abide it, and for want of other language cried, 'Ah! ah! ah! ha!!' Fain he would have spit and could not, so that he was fain to swallow down such liquor as he never tasted the like.

When he had a pretty while been washed in this sort, at the length he crouched down upon his knees, yielding himself to their favour, which the maidens perceiving pulled the gag out of his mouth. He had no sooner the liberty of his tongue but that he cursed and swore like a devil. The maids, that could scant stand for laughing, at last asked how he liked his washing.

'Washing!' quoth he, 'I was never thus washed, nor ever met with such barbers since I was born.' 'Let me go,' quoth he, 'and I will give you whatsoever you will demand,' wherewith he cast them an English crown.

'Nay,' quoth one of the maids, 'you are yet but washed, but we will shave you ere ye go.'

'Sweet maids,' quoth he, 'pardon my shaving, let it suffice that you have washed me. If I have done a trespass to your trade, forgive it me, and I will never hereafter offend you.'

'Tush,' said the maids, 'you have made our wheels cast their bands and bruised the teeth of our cards in such sort as the offence may not be remitted without great penance. As for your gold, we regard it not. Therefore, as you are perfumed fit for the dogs, so we enjoin you this night to serve all our hogs, which penance if you will swear with all speed to perform we will let you loose. '

Will Summers stripped up his sleeves very orderly, and clapped an apron about his motley hosen, and taking a pail, served the hogs handsomely. When he came to the court, he showed to the King all his adventure among the weaver's maidens, whereat the King and Queen laughed heartily.

JACK OF NEWBURY

Colliers and mine-workers should be well acquainted with all the philosophical secrets of the Earth, because they have deeper knowledge in it than any others.

CONCEITS, CLINCHES FLASHES AND WHIMZIES

Elizabethan Humour

One making a long and tedious speech to a grave counsellor, in the conclusion thereof made an apology to excuse himself for being so troublesome – who gave him this answer: 'I'll assure you sir, you have not been troublesome to me at all, for the time that you were speaking my mind was of another matter!'

A BANQUET OF JESTS

One said that tall men of all others were most happy, because they were nearer heaven than all other men.

CONCEITS, CLINCHES, FLASHES AND WHIMZIES

An oculist is excellent at sleight of hand: for, if he undertake to cure a blind man, he will so do it that the patient shall see.

CONCEITS, CLINCHES, FLASHES AND WHIMZIES

A Physiognomer

One that was a great practitioner of Physiognomy, reading late at night, happened upon a place which said hairy men for the most part are dull, and a thick, long, beard betokened a fool.

He took down his looking-glass in one hand, and held the candle in the other to observe the growth and fashion of his own; holding it so long, till at length by accident he fired it. Whereupon he wrote on the margin (as well he might), 'it has been proven' *Probatum est.*

A BANQUET OF JESTS

A scholar having married a young wife, and being still at his book, preferring his serious study before dalliance with her, as she was one day wantoning whilst he was reading:

'Sir,' saith she, 'I could wish my self that I had been made a book, for then you would be still poring upon me, and I should never night or day be out of your fingers.'

'So would I, sweet-heart,' answered he, 'so I might choose what book.'

To whom she again answered, 'And what book would you wish me to be?'

'Marry, sweet wife,' saith he, 'An Almanack – for so I might have every year a new one.'

A BANQUET OF JESTS

Of a Scholler and his Sweet-heart

A young scholar lighting upon a handsome wench had agreed with her to carry her into the College, for which purpose he had provided a large basket, wherein he put her and covered her with roots, lettuce, and such like commodities, and so carried it in upon his shoulders, as though he brought some provision for the house.

But by the way, the bottom of the basket failed, and the wench's legs did hang down and were visible as high as the garter.

One meeting him asked him what burden he was carrying to the College, who answered, 'Roots and herbs for salads'.

'And I commend thee,' quoth the other, 'that thou hast the wit to provide such good flesh for thy salads.'

A BANQUET OF JESTS

Elizabethan Humour

How Tarlton deceived a doctor of physicke

Tarlton, to satisfy the humours of certain gentlemen his familiar acquaintance, went about for to try the skill of a simple doctor of physic, that dwelt not far from Islington. And thus it was, he took a fair urinal, and filled it half full of good wine, and bore it to the doctor, saying it was a sick man's water.

He viewed it, and tossing it up and down, as though he had great knowledge, quoth he: 'The patient, whose water it is, is full of gross humours, and hath great need of purging, and to be let some ten ounces of blood.'

'No, you dunce!' replied Tarlton, 'it is good.' And with that drunk it off and threw the urinal at his head.

TARLTONS JESTS

VROSCOPY

THE CIRCLE OF URINARY COLOURS.

A Coachman

A mad fellow – a Coachman – about the towne being drunk, fell from the seat where he sat, and the wheel running over him broke one of his legs, the anguish of which drove him into a fever: but being well recovered of them both, he had an humour to go and prove all the prime Doctors of the town, and try whether by his water they could tell his profession, or his misfortune, or the disease that before had troubled him.

He being then in perfect health, his water was carried to many, and all that saw it concluded that he that sent it was a sound man, but could proceed no further. Therefore, his opinion was that all Physicians are fools and not one learned man amongst them. This being told an ancient, grave Doctor that practised about the City by one of the Coachman's acquaintance by whom he had understood every particular before related, he wrought with him to persuade the Coachman to bring his water to him, which took effect.

But in their journey toward the Doctor, they drinking somewhat hard, the Coachman carrying his urinal empty, pissed it full, which his friend seeing; 'Fie,' saith he, 'carry not all this water along for shame; pour out half at least, otherwise he will perceive we have been drinking.' The Coachman was persuaded, and did so.

On they went, and whilst the Coachman stayed below, his friend went up to see if the Doctor were at leisure, and told him all that past by the way. This done, the patient is called up, who presents his urinal to the Doctor, with many a low congee [bow] outwardly, though scoffing inwardly.

The Doctor he turns and tosses the glass, sometimes chafing it against the fire, then again holds it up to the light. At last he breaks into these words; 'I perceive by this water, that he that made it was a Carter, or Carman.'

'Truly,' (saith he), 'if it please your worship, you come the nearest of all the Doctors I have tried yet, and yet you are wide from the mark.'

'Wilt thou tell me that?' saith the Doctor. 'Sure I am, he is one that gets his living by the whip.'

'Therein you are right again,' answered the other, 'for to tell you true, he was a Coachman.'

'Very good,' saith the Doctor. 'Now, this Carter being drunk, fell from his cart, and the wheel ran over him and broke his leg.'

'You are right in all things sir, if you would change the "cart", and the "Carter" into "coach" and "Coachman".'

'Interrupt me not' saith the Doctor. 'This Carter breaking his leg, fell into a dangerous fever, of which he is since recovered.'

'Good your worship, no more Carter, nor cart, if you love me; for of my knowledge he was a *Coachman*, and fell from his *coach!*'

'His Coach?' saith the Doctor, still looking upon the urine: 'I prethee, truly resolve me – is here *all* the water that was made?'

'No indeed,' saith the fellow, 'I poured out half, by the way.'

'Nay, I thought as much! Then there went away the other two wheels,' saith the Doctor, 'for there cannot be above two contained in this urinal.'

The Coachman admires his cunning, departs satisfied with his skill, saith he shall have his custom, with all comrades; and vowed only for his sake to speak well of Doctors ever after.

A BANQUET OF JESTS

One being dissuaded from marrying a woman because she was no wiser, made this answer: 'I desire that the wife whom I am to marry should have no more wit than to be able to distinguish her husband's bed from another man's.'

A BANQUET OF JESTS

Of the Innholders wyfe and her ii lovers

Near unto Florence dwelled an innholder, whose wife was not very dangerous of her tail. Upon a night as she was a-bed with one of her lovers, there came an other to have lain with her. When she heard him come up the ladder, she met him and bade him go thence, for she had no time than to fulfil his pleasure. But for all her words he would not go away, but still pressed to come in.

So long they stood chiding, that the goodman husband came upon them, and asked why they brawled so. The woman, not unprovided of a deceitful answer, said: 'Sir, this man would come in perforce to slay or mischief an other, that is fled in to our house for succour, and hitherto I have kept him back.'

When he, that was within, heard her say so, he began to pluck up his heart and say, he would be a wreked [revenged] on him without. And he that was without, made a face as he would kill him that was within.

The foolish man, her husband, inquired the cause of their debate, and took upon him to set them at one. And so the good silly man spake and made the peace between them both; yea, and farther he gave them a gallon of wine, adding to his wife's adultery the loss of his wine!

MERY TALES, WITTIE QUESTIONS, AND QUICKE ANSWERES

Of the wife who lay with her 'prentice and caused him to beat her husband disguised in her rayment

A wife there was, which had appointed her 'prentice to come to her bed in the night, which servant had long wooed her to have his pleasure.

In the night, her husband lying by her, she caught him by the hand and held him fast, and incontinent wakened her husband, and said: 'Sir, it is so ye have a false and untrue servant, which is William your 'prentice, and hath long wooed me to have his pleasure; and because I could not avoid his importunate request, I have appointed him this night to meet me in the garden in the arbour; and if ye will array yourself in mine array and go thither, ye shall see the proof thereof; and ye may rebuke him as ye think best by your discretion.'

This husband, thus advertised by his wife, put upon him his wife's raiment and went to the arbour; and when he was gone thither the 'prentice came in to bed to his mistress, where for a season they were both content and pleased each other by the space of an hour or two.

But when she thought time convenient, she said to the 'prentice: 'Now, go thy way in to the arbour, and meet him and take a good waster [cudgel] in thy hand, and say thou did it but to prove whether I would be good woman or no; and reward him as thou thinkest best.'

This 'prentice doing after his mistress' counsel went in to the arbour, where he found his master in his mistress' apparel and said : 'Ah! Thou harlot, art thou comen hither? Now I see well, if I would be false to my master, thou wouldst be a strong whore; but I had rather thou were hanged than I would do him so traitorous a deed. Therefore I shall give thee some punishment, as thou like an whore hast deserved.' And therewith lapt him well about the shoulders and back, and gave him a dozen or two good stripes.

The master, feeling himself somewhat to smart, said : 'Peace, William, mine own true good servant; for God's sake, hold thy hands, for I am thy master and not thy mistress!'

'Nay, whore!' quoth he, 'Thou knowest thou art but an harlot, and I did but to prove thee.' And smote him again.

'Hold! Hold!' quoth the master, 'I beseech thee, no more: for I am not she: for I am thy master, for I have a beard.' And therewith he spared his hand and felt his beard.

'Good master!' quoth the 'prentice, 'I cry you mercy!'

And then the master went unto his wife, and she asked him how he had sped.

And he answered: 'I wys, wife, I have been shrewdly beaten. Howbeit I have cause to be glad: for I thank God I have as true a wife and as true a servant as any man hath in England!'

By this tale ye may see that it is not wisdom for a man to be ruled alway after his wife's counsel

AN HUNDRED MERRY TALES

A man with one eye

A fellow with one eye being abroad about his business, his wife in his absence entertained another man. But so it happened that her husband came home and entered the room before the loving couple expected him. At whose presence the woman, greatly abashed, rose up, and running to her husband, clapt her hand upon the eye he could see with, saying, 'Husband, I dreamt just now that you could see as well with the other eye, as with this: pray tell me.'

Meanwhile her friend slipped out of doors.

A BANQUET OF JESTS

Of the fryer that confessed the woman

As a fair young woman of the town of Amilie confessed her to a friar, he began to burn so in concuspiscence of the flesh, that he enticed her to consent to his will. And they agreed, that she should feign herself sick, and send for him to shrive her.

Within three days after, she feigned herself sick, and lay down in her bed, and sent for the same friar to shrive her. When the friar was come, and everybody voided out of the chamber, he went to bed to the woman, and there lay a long space with her.

Her husband, suspecting so long a confession, came into the chamber: whose sudden coming so sore abashed the friar, that he went his way and left his breche [pants] behind him lying on the bed.

When her husband saw the breche, he said aloud, 'This was not a friar but an adulterer.' And for great abomination of the deed he called all his household to see it.

And forthwith he went and complained to the warden of that convent, and threatened to slay him that had done the deed. The warden, to appease his anger, said that such publishing was to the shame of him and his household. The man said, the breche was so openly found that he could not hide it. The warden to remedy the matter said, it was St Francis's breche, an holy relic that his brother carried thither for the woman's health, and that he and his convent would come and fetch it home with procession.

With those words the man was content. Anon, the warden and his friars, with the cross before them, and arrayed in holy vestments, went to the house and took up the breche; and two of them on a cloth of silk bore it solemnly on high between their hands, and everybody that met them knelt down and kissed it. So, with great ceremony and song, they bought it home to their convent.

MERY TALES, WITTIE QUESTIONS AND QUICKE ANSWERES

One whose name was Gun called a woman whore. She being moved at it, had him before a justice of peace about it. The justice reprov'd him for it, and deeply charged him not to call her so again.

As they were going home, the woman told him: 'Master Gun, you heard what the justice said: I hope, being so deeply charg'd, you will hence-forward give a better report.'

CONCEITS, CLINCHES, FLASHES AND WHIMZIES

One asked, wherefore a drum was in the wars. It was answered, to stir up valour in the soldiers. That is strange, said the other, for wheresoever the victory falls, the drums are sure to be beaten.

CONCEITS, CLINCHES, FLASHES AND WHIMZIES

A Papist and a Puritan being next neighbours and travelling by the high way where stood a wooden cross, the Papist put off his hat and so passed by, at which his neighbour only smiled to himself and said nothing. But walking further, and passing by a tree that stood in the way and not seeing him move to that; 'Neighbour,' (saith he), 'I pray you in courtesy, will you not resolve a question?'

'With all my heart,' replied the other, 'so that the occasion be offered you'll do me the like.'

Both are agreed. 'Now then, neighbour,' saith the Puritane, 'I would know why you did not the like reverence unto the tree that you did unto the cross being both one wood?'

'The reason of this,' (saith the other), 'you shall soon know, but one thing first I must know of you; I called upon you in the morning, and I observed you in taking leave of your wife. Why did you kiss her lips and not her tail, seeing they are both made of the one flesh?'

A BANQUET OF JESTS

A Gentleman of England travelling with his man to Rome desirous to see all fashions, but especially such rarities as were there to be seen was, by the mediation of some friends there resident, admitted into the Pope's presence: to whom His Holiness offered his foot to kiss, which the Gentleman did with great submission and reverence.

This his man seeing, and not before acquainted with the like ceremony, presently maketh what speed he can to get out of the presence; which some of the waiters, espying and suspecting his haste, stayed him and demanded the cause of his so sudden speed.

But the more they importuned him the more he

pressed to be gone; but being further urged he made this short answer. 'Truly,' saith he, 'this is the cause of my fear. That if they compel my Master, being a Gentleman, to kiss the Pope's *foot*, I fear what part they will make me kiss, being but his serving man!'

A BANQUET OF JESTS

BEING
A COLLECTION OF
Moderne Jests.
Witty Jeeres.
Pleasant Taunts.
Merry Tales.

FINIS.

Bibliography

The Art of Living in London by Henry Peacham. A late pamphlet printed in 1642.

A Banquet of Jests. First published in 1630, reprinted in five editions, and expanded to two volumes in 1640.

The Black Book's Messenger by Robert Greene. Published in 1592.

A Briefe Treatise of Naturall & Artificiall Conclusions by T. Hill. First published in 1581.

Brief Lives by John Aubrey. This is the name by which they have come to be known. Biographies by Aubrey whose seventeenth-century manuscripts were eventually transcribed and edited in the late nineteenth century.

A Caveat or Warning for Commen Cursetors by Thomas Harman. First published in 1566. A later edition in 1592 was called *The Groundwork of Cony-Catching*.

Conceits, Clinches, Flashes and Whimzies. Anonymous. First published in 1631.

Grimello's Fortunes by Nicholas Breton. Published in 1604.

The Guls Horne-booke by Thomas Dekker. First published in 1609.

An Hundred Merry Tales. Anonymous. First compiled and published *circa* 1525.

Jack of Newbury by Thomas Deloney. Published in 1597.

The Jests of Scogin, originating from *c.* 1566, but still in print in 1620.

Bibliography

Joan's Ale is New. One of the many anonymous ballads from the late sixteenth century.

Manningham's Diary for 1602. Contains this apocryphal story in a manuscript transcribed and printed in 1831.

Mery Tales of the Mad Men of Gottam. Anonymous. Still in print in 1630.

Mery Tales, Wittie Questions, and Quicke Answeres. Anonymous. First published 1567.

A Nest of Ninnies by Robert Armin. First published in 1608.

Pasquils Jests. First published under the pseudonym of 'Pasquil' in 1604.

The Philosopher's Banquet, containing *Certayne Conceyts and Jeasts.* Anonymous. First published in 1614.

Pierce Pennilesse his Supplication to the Devil by Thomas Nashe. First published in 1592.

The Second Part of Conny-Catching by Robert Greene. Published c. 1591.

Tarltons Jests. An anonymous, posthumous, compilation of Richard Tarlton's jests (d. 1589). First published 1611, but still in print in 1628.

Taylors Wit and Mirth by John Taylor, 'The Water Poet'. Published in 1626.

The Third and last Part of Conny-Catching by Robert Greene. Published in 1592.

The Unfortunate Traveller by Thomas Nashe. First published in 1594.